STATISTICS
FOR
ENGINEERS

Also from the same publisher:

White, Yeats and Skipworth: TABLES FOR STATISTICIANS
Francis: ADVANCED LEVEL STATISTICS — An Integrated Approach
Montagnon: STATISTICS FOR MANAGERS

STATISTICS
FOR
ENGINEERS

A. Greer

C.Eng., M.R.Ae.S.
Senior Lecturer
Gloucester City College of Technology

Stanley Thornes (Publishers) Ltd

First published in 1979 by
Stanley Thornes (Publishers) Ltd
Old Station Drive
Leckhampton
CHELTENHAM GL53 0DN
England

Reprinted 1987

ISBN 0 85950 495 6

Text set in 11/12 pt Baskerville at the Alden Press, Oxford, London and Northampton
Printed and bound in Great Britain at The Bath Press, Avon

Preface

This book covers all the objectives laid down in the Level III standard T.E.C. unit in Statistics (TEC U77/426). In addition, the first chapter revises the topics in Statistics dealt with in Level I and Level II standard mathematics units.

As far as has been possible, the examples and exercises have been given a practical flavour. The aim has been to provide the student with sufficient basic statistical theory so that he will be able to tackle more specialist topics such as Quality Control and Operational Research, etc.

A. Greer   Gloucester, 1979

Contents

Useful Formulae

ARITHMETIC MEAN

$$\bar{x} = \frac{\sum x}{n}$$

x = measured observations
n = number of observations
$\bar{x}$ = arithmetic mean

MEAN OF A FREQUENCY DISTRIBUTION

$$\bar{x} = \frac{\sum fx}{\sum f}$$

f = frequency
x = measured observations
$\bar{x}$ = arithmetic mean

MEAN OF A FREQUENCY DISTRIBUTION USING AN ASSUMED MEAN

$$\bar{x}_c = \frac{\sum fx_c}{\sum f}$$

$\bar{x}$ = assumed mean + $\bar{x}_c$ × unit size

f = frequency
x_c = coded values of observations
$\bar{x}_c$ = coded value of the mean
$\bar{x}$ = arithmetic mean

RANGE

Range = largest observation − smallest observation

STANDARD DEVIATION

$$\sigma = \sqrt{\frac{\sum x^2}{n} - \bar{x}^2}$$

σ = standard deviation
x = measured observations
n = number of observations
$\bar{x}$ = arithmetic mean

STANDARD DEVIATION OF A FREQUENCY DISTRIBUTION

$$\sigma = \sqrt{\frac{\sum fx^2}{\sum f} - \bar{x}^2}$$

σ = standard deviation
x = measured observations
f = frequency
$\bar{x}$ = arithmetic mean

STANDARD DEVIATION USING AN ASSUMED MEAN

$$\sigma_c = \sqrt{\frac{\sum fx_c^2}{\sum f} - \bar{x}_c^2}$$

$$\sigma = \sigma_c \times \text{unit size}$$

σ_c = coded value of standard deviation

x_c = coded value of observation

f = frequency

$\bar{x}_c$ = coded value of the mean

SIMPLE PROBABILITY

$$\text{Pr(event occurring)} = \frac{\text{possibility of event occurring}}{\text{total possibilities}}$$

$$\text{Total probability} = 1$$

EMPIRICAL PROBABILITY

$$P = \frac{\text{total number of occurrences of the event}}{\text{total number of trials}}$$

MULTIPLICATION LAW OF PROBABILITY FOR INDEPENDENT EVENTS

$$\text{Pr}(E_1 E_2 \ldots E_n) = \text{Pr}(E_1) \times \text{Pr}(E_2) \times \ldots \text{Pr}(E_n)$$

$\text{Pr}(E_1)$ = probability of first event occurring

$\text{Pr}(E_2)$ = probability of second event occurring

$\text{Pr}(E_1 E_2 \ldots E_n)$ = probability that all of the events occur and E_1, $E_2 \ldots E_n$ are independent events

MULTIPLICATION LAW OF PROBABILITY FOR DEPENDENT EVENTS

$$\text{Pr}(E_1 E_2) = \text{Pr}(E_1) \times \text{Pr}(E_1/E_2)$$

$\text{Pr}(E_1)$ = probability of first event occurring

$\text{Pr}(E_1/E_2)$ = probability that E_2 occurs given that E_1 has occurred

$\text{Pr}(E_1 E_2)$ = the probability that both E_1 and E_2 occur, E_1 and E_2 being dependent events

ADDITION LAW OF PROBABILITY FOR MUTUALLY EXCLUSIVE EVENTS

$$\text{Pr}(E_1 + E_2 + \ldots E_n) = \text{Pr}(E_1) + \text{Pr}(E_2) + \ldots \text{Pr}(E_n)$$

$\text{Pr}(E_1 + E_2 + \ldots E_n)$ = probability that one of the events happens, E_1, $E_2 \ldots E_n$ being mutually exclusive events

$\text{Pr}(E_1)$ = probability that E_1 occurs

$\text{Pr}(E_2)$ = probability that E_2 occurs.

ADDITION LAW OF PROBABILITY FOR NON-MUTUALLY EXCLUSIVE EVENTS

$$\Pr(E_1 + E_2) = \Pr(E_1) + \Pr(E_2) - \Pr(E_1 E_2)$$

$$\Pr(E_1 + E_2 + E_3) = \Pr(E_1) + \Pr(E_2) + \Pr(E_3) - \Pr(E_1 E_2) - \Pr(E_1 E_3)$$
$$- \Pr(E_2 E_3) + \Pr(E_1 E_2 E_3)$$

$$\Pr(E_1 + E_2 + E_3) = 1 - [\Pr(\bar{E}_1) \times \Pr(\bar{E}_2) \times \Pr(\bar{E}_3)]$$

$\Pr(E_1 + E_2 + E_3) = $ probability that one of the events happens and E_1, E_2 and E_3 are non-mutually exclusive events

$\Pr(\bar{E}_1) = $ probability of E_1 not happening

$\Pr(\bar{E}_2) = $ probability of E_2 not happening

COMPONENTS IN SERIES

$$\Pr(ABC) = \Pr(A) \times \Pr(B) \times \Pr(C)$$

COMPONENTS IN PARALLEL

$$\Pr(A + B + C) = 1 - [\Pr(\bar{A}) \times \Pr(\bar{B}) \times \Pr(\bar{C})]$$

BINOMIAL DISTRIBUTION

$$(q + p)^n = q^n + nq^{n-1}p + \frac{n(n-1)}{2!} q^{n-2}p^2 + \ldots + p^n$$

Number of defectives	Probability
0	q^n
1	$nq^{n-1}p$
2	$\dfrac{n(n-1)}{2!} q^{n-2}p$
	etc.

$n = $ the number of items in the sample

$p = $ the probability of finding a defective item in a single trial

$q = $ the probability of finding a good item in a single trial

$p + q = 1$

POISSON DISTRIBUTION

Number of defectives	Probability
0	$\Pr(0) = e^{-\lambda}$
1	$\Pr(1) = \lambda e^{-\lambda} = \lambda \Pr(0)$
2	$\Pr(2) = \dfrac{\lambda^2}{2!} e^{-\lambda} = \dfrac{\lambda}{2} \Pr(1)$
	etc.

$\lambda = $ average occurrence of the event
$= np$

$n = $ number of items in the sample

$p = $ probability of finding a defective item in a single trial

NORMAL DISTRIBUTION

$$u = \frac{x - \bar{x}}{\sigma}$$

u = standarised variable
x = value of the variate
$\bar{x}$ = arithmetic mean
σ = standard deviation

DISTRIBUTION OF SAMPLE MEANS

$$\bar{x} = \mu$$

$$s_{\bar{x}} = \frac{\sigma}{\sqrt{n}} \sqrt{\frac{n_p - n}{n_p - 1}}$$

For an infinite population:

$$s_{\bar{x}} = \frac{\sigma}{\sqrt{n}}$$

μ = the mean of the population
$\bar{x}$ = the mean of the sampling distribution
σ = the standard deviation of the population
n = the number of items in each sample
n_p = the number of items in the population
$s_{\bar{x}}$ = the standard deviation of the sampling distribution

CONFIDENCE LIMITS

$$\text{Confidence limit} = \bar{x} \pm \frac{u_c \sigma}{\sqrt{n}}$$

For $n < 30$,

$$\text{Confidence limit} = \bar{x} \pm \frac{t_c s}{\sqrt{n - 1}}$$

$\bar{x}$ = mean of the sample
u_c = value of u corresponding to the confidence level using the normal distribution
σ = standard deviation of the population
n = number of items in the sample
t_c = value of t corresponding to the confidence level using the t-distribution

UNBIASED ESTIMATES

$$\bar{x} = \mu$$

$$\hat{s} = s \times \sqrt{\frac{n - 1}{n}}$$

If $n \geqslant 30$ then:

$$s = \sigma$$

$\bar{x}$ = mean of the sample
μ = mean of the population
s = standard deviation of the sample
n = the number of items in the sample

$\hat{s}$ = unbiased estimate of the population standard deviation

SIGNIFICANCE TESTS FOR COMPARING MEANS

For $n \geqslant 30$ use normal distribution with:

$$u = \frac{\bar{x} - \mu}{\sigma/\sqrt{n}}$$

$\bar{x}$ = mean of the sample
μ = mean of the population
σ = standard deviation of the population
n = number of items in the sample

For $n < 30$ and σ unknown, use the t-distribution with:

$$t = \frac{\sqrt{n-1}\,|\bar{x} - \mu|}{s}$$

$\bar{x}$ = mean of the sample
μ = mean of the population
s = standard deviation of the sample
n = number of items in the sample

SIGNIFICANCE TEST FOR DIFFERENCE BETWEEN TWO MEANS

If the standard deviation of the population is known and the normal distribution applies:

$$u = \frac{|\bar{x}_1 - \bar{x}_2|}{\sigma\sqrt{\dfrac{1}{n_1} + \dfrac{1}{n_2}}}$$

$\bar{x}_1$ = mean of the first sample
$\bar{x}_2$ = mean of the second sample
σ = standard deviation of the population
n_1 = number of the first sample
n_2 = number of the second sample

If the population standard deviation is *not* known the standard deviation for the difference of two means is:

$$\sigma_d = \sqrt{\frac{n_1 s_1{}^2 + n_2 s_2{}^2}{n_1 + n_2 - 2}}$$

$$t = \frac{|\bar{x}_1 - \bar{x}_2|}{\sigma_d\sqrt{\dfrac{1}{n_1} + \dfrac{1}{n_2}}}$$

n_1 = number in the first sample
n_2 = number in the second sample
s_1 = standard deviation of first sample
s_2 = standard deviation of second sample

SIGNIFICANCE TEST FOR PAIRED VARIATES

$$\bar{D} = \frac{\sum D}{n}$$

$$s = \sqrt{\frac{\sum D^2}{n} - \bar{D}^2}$$

$$t = \frac{\bar{D}\sqrt{n-1}}{s}$$

D = difference between each pair of values

s = standard deviation

$\bar{D}$ = mean

n = number of pairs of values

EQUATION OF A STRAIGHT LINE

$$y = a + bx$$

y = dependent variable

x = independent variable

a = intercept on the y-axis

b = gradient of the line

LEAST SQUARE LINES

The regression line for y on x is found by solving the following pair of simultaneous equations:

$$\sum y = an + b \sum x \quad [1]$$

$$\sum xy = a \sum x + b \sum x^2 \quad [2]$$

y = value of the dependent variable

x = corresponding value of the independent variable

a = intercept on the y-axis

b = gradient of the least square line

n = number of pairs of values of x and y

The regression line for x on y is found by solving the following pairs of simultaneous equations:

$$\sum x = a_1 n + b_1 \sum y \quad [1]$$

$$\sum xy = a_1 \sum y + b_1 \sum y^2 \quad [2]$$

a_1 = intercept on the x-axis

b_1 = gradient of the least square line

CORRELATION

For precise positive linear correlation $\quad r = +1$

For precise negative linear correlation $\quad r = -1$

For no linear correlation $\quad\quad\quad\quad\quad r = 0$

r = coefficient of correlation

COEFFICIENT OF CORRELATION

$$r = \sqrt{bb_1}$$

$$r = \frac{n \sum xy - (\sum x)(\sum y)}{\sqrt{[n \sum x^2 - (\sum x)^2][n \sum y^2 - (\sum y)^2]}}$$

$b = $ gradient of regression line for y on x

$b_1 = $ gradient of regression line for x on y

Chapter 1

Frequency Distributions

After reaching the end of this chapter you should be able to:

1) Distinguish between discrete and continuous variables.

2) Understand the concept of variability.

3) Make a tally chart and hence obtain a frequency distribution from raw data.

4) Determine the class boundaries and the class width.

5) Draw a histogram for both grouped and ungrouped distributions.

6) Sketch the frequency curves which occur in practice.

7) Calculate the mean and standard deviation for a frequency distribution.

8) Obtain the range for a small sample.

VARIABLES

Variables are measured quantities which can be expressed as numbers.

Discrete variables can only take certain values. For instance, the number of milling machines in a factory can only be a whole number. It cannot be a fractional amount.

Continuous variables can theoretically take any value between two end values. Suppose the diameter of a turned piece varies between 14.85 mm and 15.15 mm. The diameter can be 14.873 mm or 15.0482 mm.

VARIABILITY

Variations in size always occur when articles are manufactured. Because of the inherent variability of every manufacturing process, the articles produced by a single process will almost certainly differ from each other.

It is usually impossible to predict the value of any characteristic (i.e. a length, a diameter, etc.) on a single item. However, by considering several items a detailed knowledge of the production process may be obtained.

FREQUENCY DISTRIBUTIONS

Suppose we take 100 successive components just as they come off a machine tool and measure their lengths. We might obtain the following results:

45.02	45.01	45.01	45.01	45.01	44.98	45.00
44.98	45.01	45.01	44.98	45.03	44.99	45.01
45.01	45.03	44.99	45.02	45.01	45.01	45.00
44.99	45.01	45.00	45.00	44.97	45.00	45.00
45.00	44.99	44.98	45.02	45.04	45.01	45.01
44.97	45.00	45.00	44.99	44.99	45.00	44.99
44.99	45.00	44.98	44.99	44.98	44.99	45.03
45.00	45.00	45.01	45.02	44.98	44.99	44.97
44.99	45.00	45.00	45.03	45.01	45.00	44.98
45.02	45.00	44.99	44.97	44.98	45.02	44.96
45.03	45.01	45.02	45.02	45.00	44.99	45.00
44.96	45.01	45.01	44.99	45.03	45.03	45.04
44.98	45.00	45.01	44.98	45.00	44.99	45.01
45.01	44.99	45.00	45.00	44.99	45.03	44.99
44.99	45.02					

These figures (called the *raw data*) mean very little as they stand. Hence, we rearrange them into a frequency distribution. To do this we collect all the 44.96 mm readings together, all the 44.97 mm readings together, and so on. A tally chart (Table 1) is the best way of doing this. Each time a measurement arises a tally mark is placed opposite the appropriate measurement. The fifth tally mark is usually made in an oblique direction thus tying the tally marks into bundles of five and making for easier counting.

When the tally marks are complete the marks are counted and their numerical value recorded in the table heading 'frequency'. The frequency is the number of times each measurement occurs. From Table 1 it will be seen that the measurement 44.96 mm occurs twice (a frequency of 2), the measurement 44.97 occurs four times (a frequency of 4) and so on.

Table 1

Measurement (mm)	Number of components with this length	Frequency
44.96	11	2
44.97	1111	4
44.98	⊞⊞ ⊞⊞ 1	11
44.99	⊞⊞ ⊞⊞ ⊞⊞ ⊞⊞	20
45.00	⊞⊞ ⊞⊞ ⊞⊞ ⊞⊞ 111	23
45.01	⊞⊞ ⊞⊞ ⊞⊞ ⊞⊞ 1	21
45.02	⊞⊞ 1111	9
45.03	⊞⊞ 111	8
45.04	11	2

From the frequency distribution of Table 1 we see that most of the measurements are grouped around the 45.00 mm mark with a few measurements more widely dispersed.

CLASS BOUNDARIES

Suppose that our measuring instrument was accurate enough so that we could take readings to the nearest 0.001 mm. In obtaining the frequency distribution we would place all measurements between 44.965 mm and 44.975 mm in the class 44.97 mm. Similarly, we would place all the measurements between 44.975 mm and 44.985 mm in the class 44.98 mm.

For the 44.97 mm class, the values 44.965 mm and 44.975 mm are called the *lower* and *upper class boundaries* respectively. The difference between the upper and lower class boundaries is called the *class width*. Thus:

class width = upper class boundary − lower class boundary

Hence for the frequency distribution of Table 1 the class width for each of the classes is 0.01 mm.

THE HISTOGRAM

The histogram is a diagram which is used to represent a frequency distribution. It consists of a set of rectangles whose *areas* represent the frequencies. If the class widths are all the same then the heights of the rectangles may be taken to represent the frequencies.

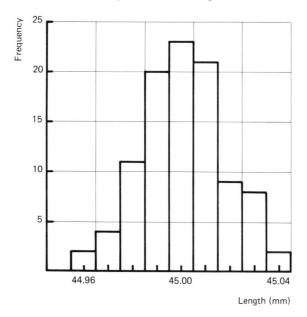

Fig. 1.1

The histogram for the frequency distribution of Table 1 is shown in Fig. 1.1. On studying the histogram the pattern of the variation becomes clear. Most of the measurements are grouped near the centre of the diagram with a few measurements more widely dispersed.

GROUPED FREQUENCY DISTRIBUTIONS

When dealing with a large amount of data it is often useful to place the information into groups. Table 2 shows a frequency distribution for the resistance of an electrical component which is being made in quantity.

Table 2

Resistance (ohms)	Frequency
87.8–88.0	4
88.1–88.3	19
88.4–88.6	45
88.7–88.9	26
89.0–89.2	6

For the first class 87.8–88.0, the lower class boundary is 87.75 and the upper class boundary is 88.05 ohms. Hence:

$$\text{class width} = 88.05 - 87.75 = 0.3 \text{ ohms}$$

(A common mistake is to state the class width as $88.0 - 87.8 = 0.2$ ohms.)

All the class widths for the grouped frequency distribution for Table 2 are the same. In drawing the histogram (Fig. 1.2) for this distribution, the

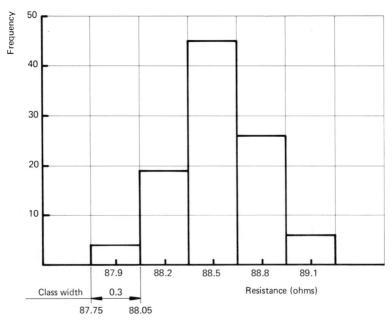

Fig. 1.2

class mid-points are used as the centres of the rectangles. Note that the extremes of each rectangle represent the upper and lower class boundaries as shown in the diagram.

GROUPED FREQUENCY DISTRIBUTIONS WITH UNEQUAL CLASS WIDTHS

Some frequency distributions are such that if equal class widths are used some of the classes will be overcrowded whilst others will be almost empty of data. The subtler aspects of the distribution may then be difficult to detect and it is better to arrange the distribution to have unequal class widths.

Consider the frequency distribution for the diameters of ball bearings shown in Table 3.

Table 3

Diameter (mm)	Frequency
28.40–28.43	4
28.44–28.45	16
28.45–28.46	35
28.47–28.48	17
28.49–28.52	5

The class widths are not all the same. For the first class and the last class the class widths are 0.04 mm whilst for the other classes, the class widths are all 0.02 mm.

When drawing the histogram it must be remembered that it is the *area of the rectangles* which represent the frequencies. If we take the unit width of a rectangle to be 0.02 mm then the widths of the rectangles for the first and last classes are each 2 units wide. The height of the first rectangle is then proportional to a frequency of 2 and the height of the last rectangle is proportional to a frequency of 2.5. The histogram then looks like Fig. 1.3 (over page).

OPEN-ENDED CLASSES

Finally consider the frequency distribution of Table 4 which deals with the heights of men working in a factory.

The first class, under 150 cm, and the last class, over 191 cm, are called open-ended classes. In drawing the histogram we have to attempt to estimate values for the unstated boundary limits. In this case we will take the limits for the first class as being 141–150 cm and the limits for the last class as 191–200. The histogram (Fig. 1.4) may then be drawn in the usual way.

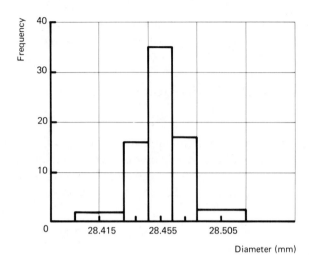

Fig. 1.3

Table 4

Height (cm)	Frequency
Under 150	3
151–160	6
161–170	16
171–180	22
181–190	12
Over 191	2

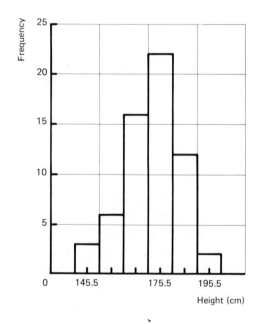

Fig. 1.4

FREQUENCY CURVES

The histogram is one way of representing a frequency distribution but it may also be represented by a frequency curve. If in Fig. 1.2 we make the class intervals smaller and smaller, the widths of the rectangles would become smaller and smaller and jumps in frequency between one class and another would become almost imperceptible. Eventually, the histogram would have the appearance of a smooth curve which is called a frequency curve.

In practice, the frequency curve is obtained by plotting the frequency of the class against the class mid-point. Fig. 1.5 shows the frequency curve for the distribution of Table 2.

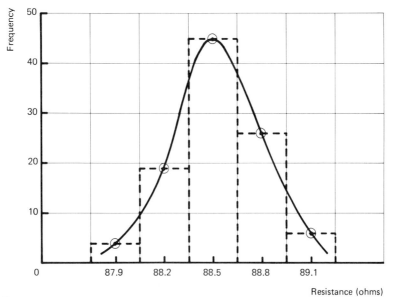

Fig. 1.5

Frequency curves which arise in practice are shown in Fig. 1.6. The curve at (a) is symmetrical about its centre-line and it is called the normal, or Gaussian, curve. Very few distributions follow the normal curve exactly but a great many distributions approximate closely to it. When a frequency distribution is obtained as a result of measurement, the frequency curve will be very nearly normal, provided enough measurements are taken (usually 100 are sufficient). The normal curve is a very important frequency curve and it is used a great deal in statistical calculations.

The U-shaped curve at (b) occurs when a minimum value is being sought. The skewed curves at (c) and (d) are approximations to the normal curve, provided the amount of skew is reasonably small. The curves (e) and (f) occur in reliability tests and also when the numbers of defective items in samples are plotted.

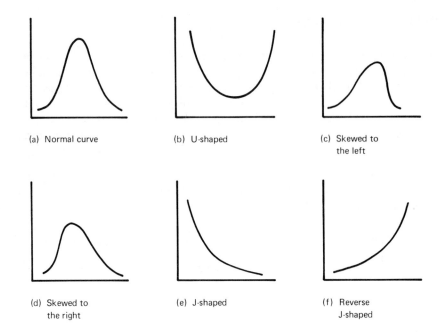

(a) Normal curve   (b) U-shaped   (c) Skewed to
                                                     the left

(d) Skewed to   (e) J-shaped   (f) Reverse
    the right   J-shaped

Fig. 1.6

THE ARITHMETIC MEAN

This the *only* average used in statistical calculations. It is found by adding
up the values of all the items in the set and dividing this sum by the number of items in the set. Thus:

$$\text{arithmetic mean} = \frac{\text{the sum of all values of the items in the set}}{\text{the number of items in the set}}$$

Symbolically,

$$\bar{x} = \frac{\Sigma x}{n}$$

EXAMPLE 1

The loads supported by 6 cables were found to be: 15.03, 15.02, 15.03,
15.02, 15.00 and 15.02 kN. What is the mean load supported by the
cables?

$$\bar{x} = \frac{\Sigma x}{n} = \frac{15.03 + 15.02 + 15.03 + 15.02 + 15.00 + 15.02}{6}$$

$$= \frac{90.12}{6} = 15.02 \text{ kN}$$

The mean load supported by the cables is 15.02 kN.

THE MEAN OF A FREQUENCY DISTRIBUTION

If $x_1, x_2, x_3 \ldots x_n$ are measured observations which have frequencies f_1, $f_2, f_3 \ldots f_n$ then the mean of the distribution is:

$$\bar{x} = \frac{\sum xf}{\sum f}$$

The symbol $\sum$ means 'the sum of' and hence $\sum xf$ tells us to multiply together corresponding values of x and f and add the results together.

EXAMPLE 2

Find the mean of the frequency distribution given in Table 1.

x	f	xf
44.96	2	89.92
44.97	4	179.88
44.98	11	494.78
44.99	20	899.80
45.00	23	1035.00
45.01	21	945.21
45.02	9	405.18
45.03	8	360.24
45.04	2	90.08
	$\sum f = 100$	$4500.09 = \sum xf$

$$\bar{x} = \frac{\sum xf}{\sum f} = \frac{4500.09}{100} = 45.000\,9 \text{ mm}$$

The mean of a grouped distribution is found by taking the values of x as the class mid-points.

EXAMPLE 3

Find the mean of the grouped distribution shown in Table 2.

Class	x	f	xf
87.8–88.0	87.9	4	351.6
88.1–88.3	88.2	19	1675.8
88.4–88.6	88.5	45	3982.5
88.7–88.9	88.8	26	2308.8
89.0–89.2	89.1	6	534.6
		100	8853.3

$$\bar{x} = \frac{\sum xf}{\sum f} = \frac{8853.3}{100} = 88.533 \text{ ohms}$$

THE CODED METHOD OF CALCULATING THE MEAN

The calculation of the mean may be speeded up by using a unit method which is often called a coded method. The first step is to choose any value in the x column as the assumed mean. This assumed mean is then used as a datum to determine the coded values. A column may then be drawn up containing the values of x in terms of units above or below the assumed mean. The calculation for Example 3 would be as follows:

Assumed mean = 88.5 ohms   unit size = 0.3 ohms

x	87.9	88.2	88.5	88.8	89.1
x_c	− 2	− 1	0	+ 1	+ 2

The coded value for $x = 87.9$ is $x_c = -2$ because this value of x is 2 units *less* than the assumed mean. The coded value for $x = 88.8$ is $x_c = +1$ because this value of x is 1 unit *greater* than the assumed mean. It is very important to assign to the coded value a plus or a minus sign depending on whether the value of x is greater or less than the assumed mean.

Although any value of x may be chosen as the assumed mean, the arithmetic will be simpler if the middle value of x is chosen. Note that the unit size of 0.3 ohms was chosen because each value of x is 0.3 ohms greater than the preceding value.

The mean may now be calculated using coded values as follows:

Class	x (class mid-point)	x_c	f	$x_c f$
87.8–88.0	87.9	− 2	4	− 8
88.1–88.3	88.2	− 1	19	− 19
88.4–88.6	88.5	0	45	0
88.7–88.9	88.8	+ 1	26	+ 26
89.0–89.2	89.1	+ 2	6	+ 12
			100	+ 11

$$\bar{x}_c = \frac{\sum x_c f}{\sum f} = \frac{11}{100} = 0.11$$

$$\bar{x} = \text{assumed mean} + \bar{x}_c \times \text{unit size}$$

$$= 88.5 + 0.11 \times 0.3 = 88.533 \text{ ohms}$$

MEASURES OF DISPERSION

The arithmetic mean locates the frequency curve along the x-axis but we now need a measure which will define the spread or dispersion of the distribution (see Fig. 1.7). The measures used in engineering are the *range* and the *standard deviation*.

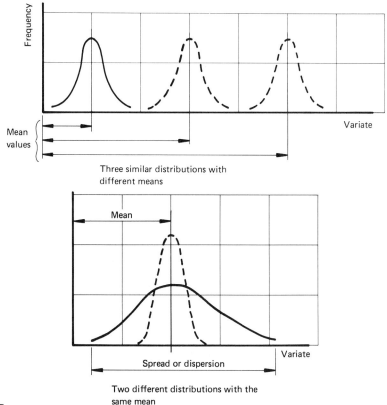

Three similar distributions with different means

Two different distributions with the same mean

Fig. 1.7

THE RANGE

The range is the difference between the largest observation in a set and the smallest observation. That is:

$$\text{Range} = \text{largest observation} - \text{smallest observation}$$

EXAMPLE 4

A sample of 5 components produced on an automatic lathe were measured with respect to their diameters. The following results were obtained: 25.01, 25.03, 25.00, 25.02 and 25.01 mm. What is the range of these measurements?

$$\text{Smallest measurement} = 25.00\,\text{mm}$$

$$\text{Largest measurement} = 25.03\,\text{mm}$$

$$\text{Range} = 25.03 - 25.00 = 0.03\,\text{mm}$$

The range gives some indication of the spread of the distribution but it depends solely on the extreme values of the data. It gives no indication of the distribution of the data and hence it is not used as a measure of dispersion for frequency distributions. However the range is a very effective measure of dispersion when dealing with small samples.

THE STANDARD DEVIATION

The most valuable and widely used measure of dispersion is the standard deviation. It is always represented by the Greek letter σ (sigma) and it is usually calculated from the formula:

$$\sigma = \sqrt{\frac{\sum x^2 f}{\sum f} - \bar{x}^2}$$

The quickest way of calculating the standard deviation is by using the coded method (see page 10).

EXAMPLE 5

Find the mean and standard deviation of the information given in the table below which relates to the diameters of ball bearings.

Diameter (mm)	7.45–7.47	7.48–7.50	7.51–7.53	7.54–7.56	7.57–7.59
Frequency	16	34	28	18	4

Class	x	x_c	f	$x_c f$	$x_c^2 f$
7.45–7.47	7.46	− 2	16	− 32	64
7.48–7.50	7.49	− 1	34	− 34	34
7.51–7.53	7.52	0	28	0	0
7.54–7.56	7.55	+ 1	18	+ 18	18
7.57–7.59	7.58	+ 2	4	+ 8	16
			100	− 40	132

Assumed mean = 7.52 mm   Unit size = 0.03 mm

$$\bar{x}_c = \frac{\sum x_c f}{\sum f} = \frac{-40}{100} = -0.4$$

$$\bar{x} = \text{assumed mean} + \text{unit size} \times \bar{x}_c$$

$$= 7.52 + 0.03 \times (-0.4)$$

$$= 7.52 - 0.012$$

$$= 7.508 \text{ mm}$$

$$\sigma_c = \sqrt{\frac{\sum x_c^2 f}{\sum f} - \bar{x}_c^2} = \sqrt{\frac{132}{100} - (-0.4)^2}$$

$$= \sqrt{1.32 - 0.16} = \sqrt{1.16} = 1.077$$

$$\sigma = \text{unit size} \times \sigma_c$$

$$= 0.03 \times 1.077 = 0.0323 \text{ mm}$$

A rough check on the calculated value of the standard deviation may be obtained by dividing the range of the given data by 6. Thus, for Example 5,

$$\text{range of data} = 7.595 - 7.445 = 0.15 \text{ mm}$$

$$\text{rough value of standard deviation} = \frac{0.15}{6} = 0.025 \text{ mm}$$

This rough value is some way from the calculated value but it does show that the calculated value is of the right order.

Note that the values of x used in the calculation are the mid-points of the various classes.

EXERCISE 1

1) The data below were obtained by measuring the frequencies (in kilo-hertz) of 60 tuned circuits. Construct a frequency distribution for the classes 12.24–12.26, 12.27–12.29 kHz, etc. and hence draw a histogram to represent this distribution.

12.37	12.29	12.40	12.41	12.31	12.35	12.37	12.35	12.33
12.36	12.32	12.36	12.40	12.38	12.33	12.35	12.30	12.30
12.34	12.39	12.43	12.32	12.27	12.32	12.41	12.40	12.37
12.40	12.35	12.34	12.38	12.43	12.36	12.35	12.26	12.28
12.36	12.24	12.42	12.39	12.44	12.42	12.28	12.25	12.34
12.33	12.32	12.39	12.38	12.27	12.35	12.35	12.34	12.36
12.36	12.32	12.31	12.35	12.29	12.30			

What is the class width of each of the classes?

2) A large transport firm had 70 lorries in different parts of the country. It wished to compile a table showing the distance travelled by each lorry in a particular period. The following information was obtained by the inspectors who checked the speedometers and recorded the distance travelled by each lorry.

Kilometres (hundreds) which each lorry travelled

10 12 30 56 57 36 27 32 57 20 15 50 49 46 21 69 55 42 60
45 35 47 22 45 44 31 67 43 17 54 49 56 51 55 29 65 23 55
46 66 40 63 24 33 62 58 15 57 64 37 38 48 27 28 59 25 52
47 26 63 30 31 31 34 65 41 16 28 39 46

(a) Draw up a frequency distribution for the classes 0–9, 10–19, 20–29, etc.

(b) Draw a histogram to represent the frequency distribution.

3) The table below shows the number of defective items found in samples of 120 items.

Number of defective items	Number of samples (frequency)
0	75
1	62
2	32
3	16
4	9
5	6

Draw a histogram to represent this information.

4) The data below gives the diameters of machined parts:

Diameter (mm)	Frequency
14.96–14.98	3
14.99–15.01	8
15.02–15.04	12

Write down:

(a) The upper and lower class boundaries for the second class.

(b) The class width of the classes shown in the table.

5) Five packets of chemical have a mass of 20.01 grams, 3 have a mass of 19.98 grams and 2 have a mass of 20.03 grams. What is the mean mass of the packets?

6) The heights of 5 men are: 177.8 cm, 175.3 cm, 174.8 cm, 179.1 cm and 176.5 cm. Calculate the mean height.

7) Each of 200 similar engine components are measured correct to the nearest millimetre and recorded as follows:

Length (mm)	Frequency
198	8
199	30
200	132
201	24
202	6

Calculate the mean length of the 200 components.

8) The resistances of 100 electrical components were measured with the following results:

Resistance (Ω)	Frequency
150–154	8
155–159	16
160–164	43
165–169	29
170–174	4

Calculate the mean resistance.

9) The diameters of 200 ball bearings were measured with the following results:

Diameter (mm)	Number
5.94–5.96	8
5.97–5.99	37
6.00–6.02	90
6.03–6.05	52
6.06–6.08	13

Calculate the mean diameter correct to 3 decimal places.

10) A sample of 5 components were taken from the hopper of an automatic lathe. Their diameters were measured and found to be 26.01, 26.00, 26.03, 25.98 and 25.99 mm. Calculate the range for this sample.

11) Calculate the mean and standard deviation for the following information:

Length (mm)	Frequency
167	2
168	8
169	15
170	6
171	3

12) Calculate the mean and standard deviation for the following frequency distribution:

Diameter (mm)	Frequency
11.46	1
11.47	4
11.48	12
11.49	15
11.50	11
11.51	6
11.52	3
11.53	1

13) Find the mean and standard deviation for the following distribution.

Height (cm)	Frequency
153–157	4
158–162	11
163–167	20
168–172	24
173–177	17
178–182	4

14) The table below shows a frequency distribution for the lifetime of cathode-ray tubes.

Lifetime (hours)	400–499	500–599	600–699	700–799	800–899
Frequency	14	50	82	46	8

15) The table below shows the distribution of maximum loads supported by certain cables manufactured by the Steel Wire Company.

Maximum load (kN)	Number of cables
84–88	4
89–93	10
94–98	24
99–103	34
104–108	28
109–113	12
114–118	6
119–123	2

Calculate the mean and standard deviation for this distribution.

Chapter 2   **Probability**

After reaching the end of this chapter you should be able to:

1) Define probability and understand that the total probability is unity.

2) Calculate simple probabilities.

3) Distinguish between dependent and independent events.

4) State the addition law of probabilities for mutually exclusive and non-mutually exclusive events.

5) State the multiplication laws of probabilities.

6) Calculate successive probabilities using **4** and **5**.

SIMPLE PROBABILITY

If a coin is tossed it will come down heads or tails. There are only these two possibilities. The probability of obtaining a head in a single toss of the coin is one possibility out of two possibilities. We write this:

$$\Pr(\text{heads}) = \frac{\text{possibility of a head}}{\text{total possibilities}} = \frac{1}{2}$$

When we work out a probability in this way we say that we have obtained a theoretical probability.

When we roll a die (plural dice) we can get one of six possible scores, 1, 2, 3, 4, 5 or 6. The probability of scoring 3 in a single roll of the die is one possibility out of a total of six possibilities. Hence:

$$\Pr(\text{three}) = \frac{1}{6}$$

There are 52 playing cards in a pack. When we cut the pack we can get one of the 52 cards, hence the total possibilities are 52. Since there are 4 aces in the pack,

$$\Pr(\text{ace}) = \frac{4}{52} = \frac{1}{13}$$

EXAMPLE 1

20 discs are marked with the numbers 1 to 20 inclusive. They are placed in a box and one disc is drawn from it. What is the probability that the number on the disc will be a multiple of 5?

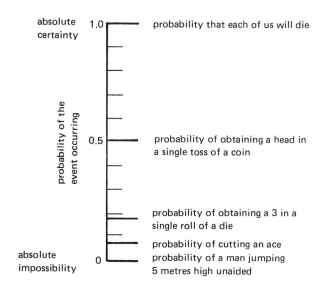

Fig. 2.1.　Probability scale

Any of the numbers, 5, 10, 15 and 20 is a multiple of 5. Hence the number of ways in which a multiple of 5 can occur is 4. The total possibilities are 20. Hence:

$$\text{Pr(multiple of 5)} = \frac{4}{20} = \frac{1}{5}$$

THE PROBABILITY SCALE

When an event is absolutely certain to happen we say that the probability of it happening is 1. Thus the probability that one day each of us will die is 1.

When an event can never happen we say that the probability of it happening is 0. Thus the probability that any one of us can jump a height of 5 metres unaided is 0.

All probabilities must, therefore, have a value between 0 and 1. They can be expressed as either a fraction or a decimal. Thus:

$$\text{Pr(head)} = \frac{1}{2} = 0.5$$

$$\text{Pr(ace)} = \frac{1}{13} = 0.077$$

Probabilities can be expressed on a probability scale (Fig. 2.1).

TOTAL PROBABILITY

If we toss a coin it will come down either heads or tails. That is:

$$Pr(\text{heads}) = \frac{1}{2}$$

$$Pr(\text{tails}) = \frac{1}{2}$$

The total probability, that is the probability covering all possible events, is $\frac{1}{2} + \frac{1}{2} = 1$. Another way of saying this is

$$Pr(\text{success}) + Pr(\text{failure}) = 1$$

Thus the probability of cutting an ace $= \frac{1}{13}$. The probability of not cutting an ace is $1 - \frac{1}{13} = \frac{12}{13}$.

EXAMPLE 2

A bag contains 5 blue balls, 3 red balls and 2 black balls. A ball is drawn at random from the bag. Calculate the probability that it will be:
(a) blue   (b) red   (c) not black.

$$\text{(a) } Pr(\text{blue}) = \frac{5}{10} = 0.5$$

$$\text{(b) } Pr(\text{red}) = \frac{3}{10} = 0.3$$

$$\text{(c) } Pr(\text{black}) = \frac{2}{10} = 0.2$$

$$Pr(\text{not black}) = 1 - Pr(\text{black}) = 1 - 0.2 = 0.8$$

REPRESENTING PROBABILITIES BY AREAS

In Fig. 2.2 let a square having unit sides, i.e. having an area of unity, represent total probability. Inside the square draw a shape to represent the

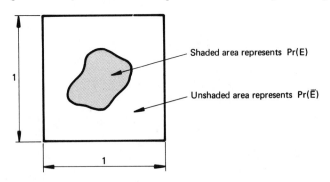

Shaded area represents $Pr(E)$

Unshaded area represents $Pr(\bar{E})$

Fig. 2.2.   Areas used to represent probabilities

probability of the event E occurring such that its area equals Pr(E). The area outside of the shape represents the probability of E not occurring which we will represent symbolically as Pr(Ē).

Thus $Pr(\bar{E}) = 1 - Pr(E)$.

EMPIRICAL PROBABILITY

Although it is possible to calculate many probabilities in the way shown above in a great many cases we have to rely on an experiment or an enquiry in order to establish the probability of an event happening.

Suppose that we have 100 ball bearings and on examining them we find that 4 are not round. What is the probability of selecting a not-round ball bearing out of the hundred?

$$\text{Total possibilities} = 100$$

Possibilities of selecting a not-round ball bearing $= 4$

$$Pr(\text{not-round}) = \frac{4}{100}$$

Empirical probabilities are therefore calculated by using the formula:

$$P = \frac{\text{total number of occurrences of the event}}{\text{total number of trials}}$$

EXAMPLE 3

From a production line in a factory, 10 successive samples each containing 50 items were checked by means of a limit gauge. The number of items failing the check were: 1, 2, 2, 4, 4, 0, 2, 3, 0, 2. What is the probability of selecting a defective item if one item is chosen at random from the production line?

$$\text{Total number of defective items} = 1 + 2 + 2 + 4 + 4 + 0 + 2 + 3 + 0 + 2$$

$$= 20$$

$$\text{Total number of items checked} = 10 \times 50 = 500$$

$$Pr(\text{selecting a defective item}) = \frac{20}{500} = 0.04$$

Empirical probabilities are often expressed as percentages and in this case we would say:

$$\text{percentage defective} = 0.04 \times 100 = 4\%$$

EXERCISE 2

1) A die is rolled. Calculate the probability that it will give:
(a) a five,

(b) a number less than 3,
(c) an even number.

2) A card is drawn from a pack of 52 playing cards. Find the probability
that it will be:

(a) the jack of hearts,
(b) an ace,
(c) an ace, king, queen or jack,
(d) the king of hearts or the ace of spades.

3) A letter is chosen from the word PITTITE. Find the probability that it
will be:

(a)   a T   (b)   a vowel.

4) A bag contains 3 red balls, 5 blue balls and 2 green balls. A ball is
drawn from the bag. Calculate the probability that it will be:

(a)   green   (b)   blue   (c)   not red.

5) Two dice are thrown together and their scores added. Find the probability that the total will be:

(a)   5   (b)   less than 5   (c)   more than 5.

6) In a factory 400 items are checked and 20 are found to be defective.
Calculate the fraction defective.

7) In a quality control investigation, ten samples each containing 15
items were checked using a plug gauge. The number of items failing the
test were 2, 0, 1, 1, 0, 0, 2, 1, 1, 0. What is the percentage defective?

8) 40 mild steel bolts became accidently mixed with 210 high tensile
steel bolts. Calculate the probability of choosing a mild steel bolt when
one bolt is selected at random from the 250 bolts.

INDEPENDENT EVENTS

An independent event is one which has no effect on subsequent events. If
a die is rolled twice what happens on the first roll does not affect what
happens on the second roll. Hence the two rolls of the die are independent
events. Similarly the events of tossing a coin then cutting a card from a
deck of playing cards are independent events because the way in which
the coin lands has no effect on the cut.

If $\Pr(E_1)$ = the probability of the first event occurring

              $\Pr(E_2)$ = the probability of the second event occurring

and $\Pr(E_1 E_2)$ = the probability that both E_1 and E_2 occur

then $\Pr(E_1 E_2)$ = $\Pr(E_1) \times \Pr(E_2)$

This is known as the multiplication law of probability. In general:

$$\Pr(E_1 E_2 \ldots E_n) = \Pr(E_1) \times \Pr(E_2) \times \ldots \Pr(E_n)$$

EXAMPLE 4

A fair coin is tossed and then a card is drawn from a pack of 52 playing cards. Find the probability that a head and an ace will result.

Let $\quad\quad\quad Pr(E_1) =$ probability of obtaining a head

Then $\quad\quad\quad Pr(E_1) = \dfrac{1}{2}$

Let $\quad\quad\quad Pr(E_2) =$ probability of cutting an ace

Then $\quad\quad\quad Pr(E_2) = \dfrac{4}{52} = \dfrac{1}{13}$

Let $\quad\quad Pr(E_1E_2) =$ probability of E_1 and E_2 occurring.

Then $\quad\quad Pr(E_1E_2) = Pr(E_1) \times Pr(E_2)$

$$= \dfrac{1}{2} \times \dfrac{1}{13} = \dfrac{1}{26}$$

Areas can again be used to illustrate the probability of both the events E_1 and E_2 occurring (Fig. 2.3).

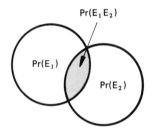

Fig. 2.3

DEPENDENT EVENTS

Consider a bag containing 3 red balls and 2 blue balls. A ball is drawn at random from the bag and not replaced. The probability that it is red is $\dfrac{3}{5}$.

Now let us choose a second ball. The probability that this is also red is $\dfrac{2}{4}$.

Hence the probability of drawing two red balls is $\dfrac{3}{5} \times \dfrac{2}{4} = \dfrac{3}{10}$. The events of drawing one red ball followed by drawing a second red ball are dependent events because the probability of the second event depends upon what happened during the first draw.

EXAMPLE 5

A bag contains 5 white balls, 3 black balls and 2 green balls. A ball is chosen from the bag and not replaced. In three draws find the probability of obtaining white, black and green in that order.

Let $\qquad Pr(E_1) = $ probability of drawing a white ball $= \dfrac{5}{10}$

$\qquad\qquad Pr(E_2) = $ probability of drawing a black ball $= \dfrac{3}{9}$

$\qquad\qquad Pr(E_3) = $ probability of drawing a green ball $= \dfrac{2}{8}$

$$Pr(E_1 E_2 E_3) = Pr(E_1) \times Pr(E_2) \times Pr(E_3) = \frac{5}{10} \times \frac{3}{9} \times \frac{2}{8} = \frac{1}{24}$$

GENERAL RULE FOR DEPENDENT EVENTS

If E_1 and E_2 are two events, the probability that E_2 occurs given that E_1 has occurred is denoted by $Pr(E_1/E_2)$. If the occurrence of E_1 affects the probability of E_2 the events E_1 and E_2 are dependent and

$$Pr(E_1 E_2) = Pr(E_1) \times Pr(E_1/E_2)$$

This rule can be extended to cover more than two dependent events.

LARGE POPULATIONS

Suppose we have a batch of 1000 items of which 50 are defective. If we select one item at random then the probability of it being defective is $\dfrac{50}{1000} = 0.05$. If this item is not replaced then the probability of selecting a second defective item is $\dfrac{49}{999} = 0.049\,05$. The probability of selecting two defective items in two successive draws is $0.05 \times 0.049\,05 = 0.002\,45$.

Although, strictly speaking, the events of selecting two defective items in two draws are dependent events, no great error is made if we consider the two events to be independent, the probability then being $0.05 \times 0.05 = 0.002\,5$.

EXAMPLE 6

A production process is known to be 10% defective. From a large batch of items produced by the process two are selected at random. What is the probability that:
(a) both will be defective,
(b) both will be good,
(c) the first is good and the second is defective, and
(d) the first is defective and the second is good?

10% defective means that the probability of selecting a defective item is

$\text{Pr(defective)} = \dfrac{10}{100} = 0.1$ and the probability of selecting a good item is

$\text{Pr(good)} = 1 - 0.1 = 0.9.$

(a) $\text{Pr(defective defective)} = \text{Pr(defective)} \times \text{Pr(defective)}$

$= 0.1 \times 0.1 = 0.01$

(b) Pr(good good) $\qquad = \text{Pr(good)} \times \text{Pr(good)}$

$= 0.9 \times 0.9 = 0.81$

(c) $\text{Pr(good defective)}$ $\qquad = \text{Pr(good)} \times \text{Pr(defective)}$

$= 0.9 \times 0.1 = 0.09$

(d) $\text{Pr(defective good)}$ $\qquad = \text{Pr(defective)} \times \text{Pr(good)}$

$= 0.1 \times 0.9 = 0.09$

Note that the total probability covering all the possible events is $0.01 + 0.81 + 0.09 + 0.09 = 1$.

MUTUALLY EXCLUSIVE EVENTS

If two events could not happen at the same time the events are said to be *mutually exclusive*. For instance suppose we want to know the probability of a 3 or a 4 occurring in a single roll of a die. In a single roll a 3 or a 4 can occur; it is not possible for a 3 and a 4 to occur together. Hence the events of throwing a 3 or a 4 in a single roll of a die are mutually exclusive. Similarly it is impossible to cut a jack and a king in a single cut of a deck of cards. Hence these two events are mutually exclusive.

If $E_1, E_2, \ldots, E_n$ are mutually exclusive events then the probability of *one* of the events happening is:

$$\text{Pr}(E_1 + E_2 + \ldots + E_n)$$
$$= \text{Pr}(E_1) + \text{Pr}(E_2) + \ldots + \text{Pr}(E_n)$$

EXAMPLE 7

A die with faces numbered 1 to 6 is rolled once. What is the probability of obtaining either a 3 or a 4.

Let the probability of obtaining a 3 be:

$$\text{Pr}(E_1) = \frac{1}{6}$$

and the probability of obtaining a 4 be:

$$\text{Pr}(E_2) = \frac{1}{6}$$

The probability of obtaining a 3 or a 4 is:

$$Pr(E_1 + E_2) = Pr(E_1) + Pr(E_2)$$
$$= \frac{1}{6} + \frac{1}{6} = \frac{1}{3}$$

EXAMPLE 8

It is known that the probability of obtaining 0 defectives in a sample of 40 items is 0.34 whilst the probability of obtaining 1 defective item in the sample is 0.46. What is the probability of:

(a) obtaining not more than 1 defective item in a sample;

(b) obtaining more than 1 defective item in a sample.

If we choose a random sample of 40 items then it may contain any number of defectives in it up to 40.

The events of drawing samples with certain numbers of defectives in them are mutually exclusive events.

(a) Pr(not more than 1 defective item)

$$= Pr(0 \text{ defective items}) + Pr(1 \text{ defective item})$$

$$= 0.34 + 0.46 = 0.80$$

(b) Since the total probability covering all possible events is 1,

$$Pr(\text{more than 1 defective item}) = 1 - 0.80 = 0.20$$

NON-MUTUALLY EXCLUSIVE EVENTS

If a pack of cards is cut once the events of drawing a jack and drawing a diamond are not mutually exclusive events because the jack of diamonds can be cut.

If $Pr(E_1)$ is the probability that an event E_1 will occur and if $Pr(E_2)$ is the probability that an event E_2 will occur then the probability that either E_1 or E_2 or both E_1 and E_2 will occur is:

$$Pr(E_1 + E_2) = Pr(E_1) + Pr(E_2) - Pr(E_1 E_2)$$

EXAMPLE 9

If E_1 is the event of drawing a jack and E_2 is the event of drawing a diamond, find the probability of drawing a jack or a diamond or both in a single cut from a deck of playing cards.

$$Pr(E_1 + E_2) = Pr(E_1) + Pr(E_2) - Pr(E_1 E_2)$$

$$= \frac{4}{52} + \frac{13}{52} - \frac{4}{52} \times \frac{13}{52}$$

$$= \frac{4}{52} + \frac{13}{52} - \frac{1}{52}$$

$$= \frac{16}{52} = \frac{4}{13}$$

The difference between mutually exclusive events and non-mutually exclusive events may be illustrated by the area diagrams of Fig. 2.4.

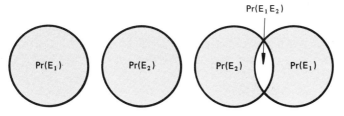

Mutually exclusive events
Shaded area gives
$Pr(E_1 + E_2) = Pr(E_1) + Pr(E_2)$

Non-mutually exclusive events
Shaded area gives
$Pr(E_1 + E_2) = Pr(E_1) + Pr(E_2) - Pr(E_1 E_2)$

Fig. 2.4

In the case of three non-mutually exclusive events:

$$Pr(E_1 + E_2 + E_3) = Pr(E_1) + Pr(E_2) + Pr(E_3) - Pr(E_1 E_2) - Pr(E_1 E_3)$$
$$- Pr(E_2 E_3) + Pr(E_1 E_2 E_3)$$

as can be seen from Fig. 2.5.

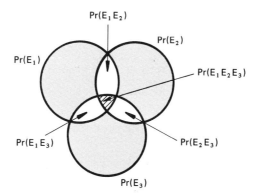

Fig. 2.5

Note that:

$$Pr(E_1 + E_2 + E_3) = 1 - Pr(\bar{E}_1 \bar{E}_2 \bar{E}_3)$$
$$= 1 - [Pr(\bar{E}_1) \times Pr(\bar{E}_2) \times Pr(\bar{E}_3)]$$

where $Pr(\bar{E}_1)$ = probability of event E_1 not happening

$$= 1 - Pr(E_1)$$

and similarly for the other probabilities.

EXAMPLE 10

Three designers A, B and C work independently on solving a particular design problem. The probability that A will solve the problem is $Pr(A) = \dfrac{2}{3}$, the probability that B will solve it is $Pr(B) = \dfrac{3}{4}$ and the probability that C will solve it is $Pr(C) = \dfrac{4}{5}$. Determine the probability that it will be solved.

Since A, B or C may solve the problem or A and B, B and C or A and C may solve it or A, B and C may solve it we have:

$$Pr(A + B + C) = Pr(A) + Pr(B) + Pr(C) - Pr(AB) - Pr(AC) - Pr(BC)$$
$$+ Pr(ABC)$$

$$= \frac{2}{3} + \frac{3}{4} + \frac{4}{5} - \left(\frac{2}{3} \times \frac{3}{4}\right) - \left(\frac{2}{3} \times \frac{4}{5}\right) - \left(\frac{3}{4} \times \frac{4}{5}\right)$$

$$+ \left(\frac{2}{3} \times \frac{3}{4} \times \frac{4}{5}\right)$$

$$= \frac{2}{3} + \frac{3}{4} + \frac{4}{5} - \frac{1}{2} - \frac{8}{15} - \frac{3}{5} + \frac{2}{5} = \frac{59}{60}$$

Alternatively,

$$Pr(\bar{A}) = 1 - \frac{2}{3} = \frac{1}{3}$$

$$Pr(\bar{B}) = 1 - \frac{3}{4} = \frac{1}{4}$$

$$Pr(\bar{C}) = 1 - \frac{4}{5} = \frac{1}{5}$$

$$Pr(A + B + C) = 1 - Pr(\bar{A}\bar{B}\bar{C})$$

$$= 1 - [Pr(\bar{A}) \times Pr(\bar{B}) \times Pr(\bar{C})]$$

$$= 1 - \left(\frac{1}{3} \times \frac{1}{4} \times \frac{1}{5}\right)$$

$$= 1 - \frac{1}{60} = \frac{59}{60}$$

The alternative method is easier arithmetically but both methods give the probability that the problem will be solved as $\dfrac{59}{60}$.

COMPONENTS IN SERIES AND PARALLEL

When components are linked in series (Fig. 2.6) it is assumed that the whole circuit fails when one of the components fail.

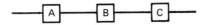

Fig. 2.6.   Components linked in series

Thus in Fig. 2.6 the events of A or B or C failing are independent events and hence the probability of the circuit functioning is:

$$Pr(ABC) = Pr(A) \times Pr(B) \times Pr(C)$$

where Pr(A), Pr(B) and Pr(C) are the probabilities of A, B and C continuing to function respectively.

EXAMPLE 11

In Fig. 2.6 the probabilities that A, B and C will continue to function for 4000 hours are 0.7, 0.6 and 0.8 respectively. Calculate the probability that the circuit will still be functioning after 4000 hours.

$$Pr(ABC) = 0.7 \times 0.6 \times 0.8 = 0.336$$

Hence the probability that the circuit will still be functioning is 33.6%. This means that it is likely that 33.6% of all the circuits made will be functioning after 4000 hours.

If all the components of a circuit are placed in parallel (Fig. 2.7) it is assumed that the circuit will still function if any of the components continues to function.

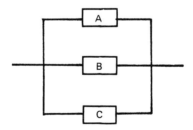

Fig. 2.7.   Components placed in parallel

Thus in Fig. 2.7 the events of A, B and C failing to function are non-mutually exclusive events because the circuit still functions if any one of the components still works. Hence the probability that the circuit functions is:

$$Pr(A + B + C) = 1 - [Pr(\bar{A}) \times Pr(\bar{B}) \times Pr(\bar{C})]$$

EXAMPLE 12

In Fig. 2.7 the probabilities that A, B and C will continue to function after 4000 hours are 0.7, 0.6 and 0.8. What is the probability that the circuit will still be functioning after 4000 hours?

$$\Pr(\bar{A}) = 1 - 0.7 = 0.3$$

$$\Pr(\bar{B}) = 1 - 0.6 = 0.4$$

$$\Pr(\bar{C}) = 1 - 0.8 = 0.2$$

$$\Pr(A + B + C) = 1 - (0.3 \times 0.4 \times 0.2)$$

$$= 1 - 0.024 = 0.976$$

Hence it is likely that 97.6% of all similar circuits will still be functioning after 4000 hours.

The placing of components in parallel is rewarded by the law of diminishing returns. Suppose that a component has a probability of 0.8 that it will survive for 2000 hours. The table below shows the probability of circuit survival after 2000 hours when several of these components are placed in parallel.

Number of components	Probability of survival after 2000 hours
1	0.80
2	$1 - 0.2^2 = 0.96$
3	$1 - 0.2^3 = 0.992$
4	$1 - 0.2^4 = 0.998\,4$
5	$1 - 0.2^5 = 0.999\,68$
6	$1 - 0.2^6 = 0.999\,936$

Using duplicate components arranged in parallel so that the system will continue to work satisfactorily even if one or more of the components fail is called *redundancy*. This method is used when high reliability is a prime consideration.

Sometimes components may be linked so that a mixture of series and parallel systems exist. The method of Example 13 may then be used.

EXAMPLE 13

The figures shown in Fig. 2.8 represent the probabilities of survival for 3000 hours for each component part of the system. Calculate the probability that the complete system will survive for 3000 hours.

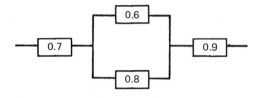

Fig. 2.8

Probability of survival up to 3000 hours:

$$= 0.7 \times [1 - (1 - 0.6)(1 - 0.8)] \times 0.9$$

$$= 0.7 \times (1 - 0.4 \times 0.2) \times 0.9$$

$$= 0.7 \times 0.92 \times 0.9$$

$$= 0.5796 \quad \text{or} \quad 57.96\%$$

THE PROBABILITY TREE

Suppose we toss a coin three times. What are the various possibilities and what are their respective probabilities? One way of finding out is to draw a probability tree.

On the first toss, the coin can show either a head or a tail. The probability of a head is $\frac{1}{2}$ and the probability of a tail is $\frac{1}{2}$. Showing possible heads by a full line and possible tails by a dotted line we may draw Fig. 2.9(a).

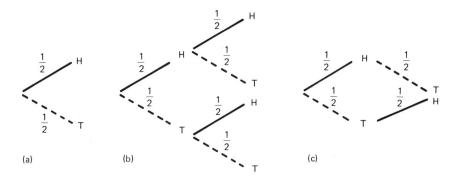

(a)   (b)   (c)

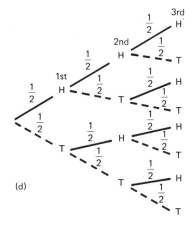

(d)

Fig. 2.9

On the second toss, for each of the branches in Fig. 2.9(a) we may also obtain either a head or a tail. Hence from each of the branches in diagram (a) we draw two more branches as shown in diagram (b). Diagram (b) tells us that the probability of a head occurring on both tosses is:

$$Pr(HH) = \frac{1}{2} \times \frac{1}{2} = \frac{1}{4}$$

one head may be obtained in one of two ways as shown in diagram (c) and hence:

$$Pr(one\ head) = \frac{1}{2} \times \frac{1}{2} + \frac{1}{2} \times \frac{1}{2} = 2 \times \frac{1}{2} \times \frac{1}{2} = \frac{1}{2}$$

Carrying on the same way the tree diagram for three tosses is as shown in diagram (d)

EXAMPLE 14

Using the tree diagram of Fig. 2.9:

(a) Write down all the possibilities that can occur when a coin is tossed three times.
(b) Calculate the probability of three heads occurring.
(c) Calculate the probability that only one head will appear.
(d) Calculate the probability that two heads will appear.

(a) The possibilities are:

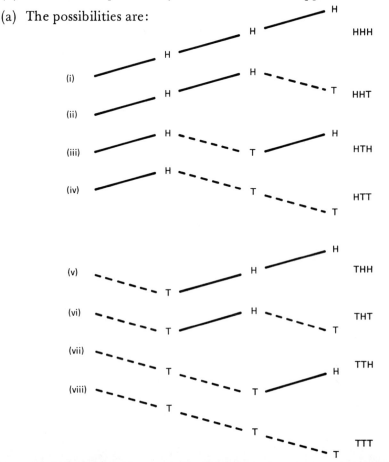

(b) Using branch (i) above,

$$Pr(HHH) = \frac{1}{2} \times \frac{1}{2} \times \frac{1}{2} = \frac{1}{8}$$

(c) Using branches (iv), (vi) and (viii) above, we see that:

$$Pr(\text{one head}) = \frac{1}{2} \times \frac{1}{2} \times \frac{1}{2} + \frac{1}{2} \times \frac{1}{2} \times \frac{1}{2} + \frac{1}{2} \times \frac{1}{2} \times \frac{1}{2}$$

$$= 3 \times \frac{1}{2} \times \frac{1}{2} \times \frac{1}{2} = \frac{3}{8}$$

(d) Using branches (ii), (iii) and (v) above, we see that

$$Pr(\text{two heads}) = \frac{1}{2} \times \frac{1}{2} \times \frac{1}{2} + \frac{1}{2} \times \frac{1}{2} \times \frac{1}{2} + \frac{1}{2} \times \frac{1}{2} \times \frac{1}{2}$$

$$= 3 \times \frac{1}{2} \times \frac{1}{2} \times \frac{1}{2} = \frac{3}{8}$$

EXAMPLE 15

A box contains 4 black and 6 red balls. A ball is drawn from the box and is not replaced. A second ball is then drawn. Find the probabilities of:

(a) red and red being drawn,
(b) black then red,
(c) red then black,
(d) black then black.

The probability tree and the probabilities required are shown in Fig. 2.10.

(a) $Pr(RR) = \frac{6}{10} \times \frac{5}{9} = \frac{1}{3}$

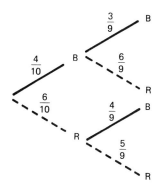

Fig. 2.10

(b) $\Pr(\text{BR}) = \dfrac{4}{10} \times \dfrac{6}{9} = \dfrac{4}{15}$

(c) $\Pr(\text{RB}) = \dfrac{6}{10} \times \dfrac{4}{9} = \dfrac{4}{15}$

(d) $\Pr(\text{BB}) = \dfrac{4}{10} \times \dfrac{3}{9} = \dfrac{2}{15}$

EXAMPLE 16

A large batch of items is known to be 10% defective. A sample of 3 items is chosen at random from the batch. Calculate the probabilities that the sample will contain:

(a) 3 defective items,
(b) 2 defective items,
(c) 1 defective item,
(d) 0 defective items.

Treating the events of selecting defective items as independent events, the probability tree is as shown in Fig. 2.11. From it we calculate the required probabilities as shown in the table below.

Number of defective items	Ways of arising	Probability of way arising
3	D D D	$0.1 \times 0.1 \times 0.1 = 0.001$
	D D G	$0.1 \times 0.1 \times 0.9 = 0.009$
2	D G D	$0.1 \times 0.9 \times 0.1 = 0.009$
	G D D	$0.9 \times 0.1 \times 0.1 = 0.009$
	D G G	$0.1 \times 0.9 \times 0.9 = 0.081$
1	G D G	$0.9 \times 0.1 \times 0.9 = 0.081$
	G G D	$0.9 \times 0.9 \times 0.1 = 0.081$
0	G G G	$0.9 \times 0.9 \times 0.9 = 0.729$

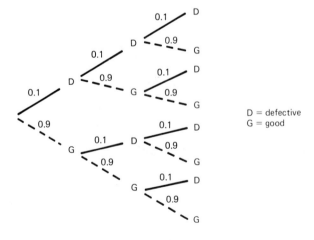

D = defective
G = good

Fig. 2.11

(a) Pr(DDD) = 0.001

(b) Pr(2 defective items) = 3 × 0.009 = 0.027

(c) Pr(1 defective item) = 3 × 0.081 = 0.243

(d) Pr(GGG) = 0.729

EXERCISE 3

1) A card is cut from a pack of playing cards. Determine the probability that it will be an ace or the king of hearts.

2) A coin is tossed and a die is rolled. Calculate the probabilities of:
(a) a tail and a 5,
(b) a head and an even number.

3) A box contains 8 red counters and 12 white ones. A counter is drawn from the box and then replaced. A second counter is then drawn. Determine the probabilities that:
(a) both counters will be red,
(b) both counters will be white,
(c) one counter will be white and the other red

4) Out of 20 components 3 are defective. Two components are chosen at random, from a large batch, for testing. What is the probability that they will both be defective?

5) A bag contains 3 red balls and 2 green balls. A ball is drawn but it is not replaced. A second ball is then drawn. Calculate the probabilities of:
(a) two red balls being chosen,
(b) two green balls being chosen,
(c) a red ball followed by a green ball being chosen.

6) Six cards marked, A, B, C, D, E and F are shuffled and two cards are drawn without replacement. What is the probability that the cards will be B and D but not necessarily in that order?

7) For the cards of question 6 find the probability that one card will be a vowel and the other will be a consonant, if the cards are replaced after drawing.

8) A box contains 3 red and 4 black balls. Draw a probability tree to show the probabilities of drawing one ball, then a second and then a third without replacement. From the tree answer the following questions:
(a) What is the probability of red, black, red?
(b) What are the chances of drawing red, red, black?
(c) What is the probability of drawing black, red, black?
(d) What is the chance of drawing black, black, black?

9) Nine cards are numbered 1 to 9 inclusive. If cards are drawn one at a time and they are not replaced find the probability that the result will be an odd card, even, even, odd, odd, even, odd, even and odd.

10) The probability of one event happening is $\dfrac{3}{5}$ and the probability of a second event happening is $\dfrac{2}{3}$. Calculate the probability that:

(a) both events will happen,
(b) one or both of the events will happen.

11) A, B and C are points in a conveyor system (Fig. 2.12). The probability of going straight on at each point is 0.6. Find the probability that a component on the conveyor will end up at

(a) X   (b) Y   and   (c) Z

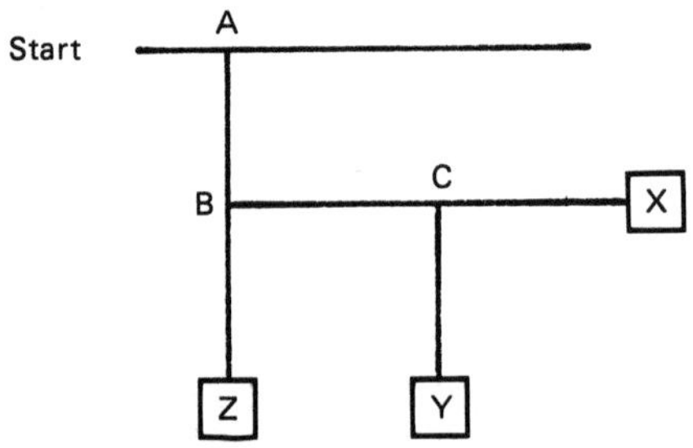

Fig. 2.12

12) In a certain factory at which 50 people work it has been found that the probabilities of absenteeism are as follows:

Number of absentees	0	1	2	3
Probability of occurrence	0.14	0.28	0.28	0.18

Find the probabilities of the number of absentees being:

(a) greater than 1,
(b) 3 or less,
(c) 2 on two successive shifts,
(d) 1 on one shift and 3 on the next shift,
(e) more than 3.

13) Two parts of a machine are manufactured independently. These two parts have a probability of 0.9 and 0.8 respectively of failing. Find the probability that

(a) neither part fails,
(b) at least one part fails,
(c) exactly one part fails.

14) A component A (Fig. 2.13) will fail one in 10 times. It is vital to the running of a machine. An identical component is fitted in parallel and

the machine will work provided that one of these components functions correctly. Find the probability that the machine keeps running.

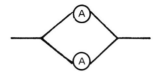

Fig. 2.13

15) In a pipe line (Fig. 2.14) the probability that a valve A will not function properly is 0.05 whilst the probability that a valve B will not function properly is 0.1. Both A and B must function properly for the system to work. Calculate the probability that the system will work.

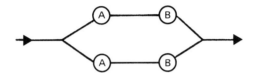

Fig. 2.14

16) Each of the elements in Fig. 2.15 has a probability of 0.6 that it will survive 5000 hours. For each of the configurations shown find the probability that the system will survive for 5000 hours.

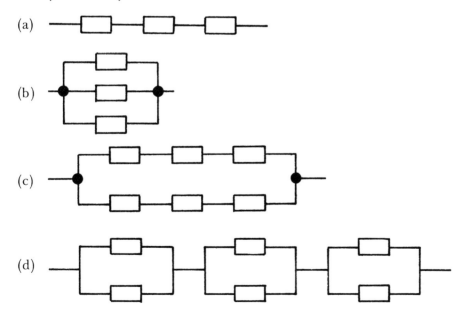

Fig. 2.15

17) The figures shown in Fig. 2.16 represent the probabilities of each

component part surviving for 2000 hours. Calculate the probability of survival for 2000 hours for the complete system.

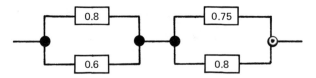

Fig. 2.16

18) Two people work independently on solving a problem. The respective probabilities that they will solve it are $\dfrac{3}{4}$ and $\dfrac{4}{5}$. What is the probability that the problem will be solved by either one of them or by both of them?

19) Four valves are linked in parallel in a pipe line. The resepctive probabilities that each will function correctly are $\dfrac{1}{3}, \dfrac{2}{5}, \dfrac{3}{4}$ and $\dfrac{5}{6}$. Calculate the probability that the pipe line will function correctly.

20) Five designers work independently on solving a design problem. The respective probabilities of each solving it are $\dfrac{1}{4}, \dfrac{1}{3}, \dfrac{1}{2}, \dfrac{3}{4}$ and $\dfrac{5}{6}$. Calculate the probability that the problem will be solved.

Chapter 3

The Binomial Distribution

After reaching the end of this chapter you should be able to:

1) Recognise the binomial situation.

2) Calculate probabilities using the formula and using tables of binomial coefficients.

3) Relate the binomial distribution to the expansion of $(q + p)^n$.

4) Relate distributions of binomial probability to histogram representation.

5) State and use formula for mean and standard deviation of a binomial distribution.

6) Solve problems involving the cumulation of terms of the binomial distribution.

REPEATED TRIALS

Suppose that it is known that 10% of the components produced on a certain machine are defective. If we choose one component at random from a large batch then the probability of it being defective is $p = \dfrac{10}{100} = 0.1$. Since the component will have to be classified as either good or defective, $p + q = 1$, where q is the probability of drawing a good component from the batch in a single trial. Hence:

$$q = 1 - p = 1 - 0.1 = 0.9$$

Now from the same large batch let us choose two components at random. Since the batch is large these may be regarded as independent events. There are three distinct possibilities as shown in Fig. 3.1 and Table 3.1.

Table 3.1

Possibility	Ways of arising		Probability of way	Probability of possibility occurring
0 defectives	good	good	$q \times q = q^2$	$q^2 = 0.9 \times 0.9 = 0.81$
1 defective	good	def.	$q \times p = pq$	$2pq = 2 \times 0.9 \times 0.1$
	def.	good	$p \times q = pq$	$= 0.18$
2 defectives	def.	def.	$p \times p = p^2$	$p^2 = 0.1 \times 0.1 = 0.01$

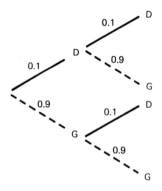

Fig. 3.1

Now let us choose three components at random. There are now four distinct possibilities as shown in Fig. 3.2 and Table 3.2.

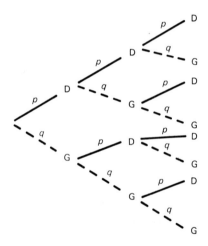

Fig. 3.2

Table 3.2

Possibility	Ways of arising	Probability of way	Probability of possibility occurring
0 defectives	good good good	$q \times q \times q$	q^3
1 defective	good def. good good good def. def. good good	$q \times p \times q$ $q \times q \times p$ $p \times q \times q$	$3q^2p$
2 defectives	good def. def. def. good def. def. def. good	$q \times p \times p$ $p \times q \times p$ $p \times p \times q$	$3qp^2$
3 defectives	def. def. def.	$p \times p \times p$	p^3

The binomial theorem states:

$$(q + p)^n = q^n + nq^{n-1}p + \frac{n(n-1)}{2!}q^{n-2}p + \frac{n(n-1)(n-2)}{3!}q^{n-3}p + \ldots$$

where

2! is factorial 2 i.e. 2×1

3! is factorial 3 i.e. $3 \times 2 \times 1$ etc.

It will be noticed that the terms of Table 2.1 are the expansion of

$$(q + p)^2 = q^2 + 2pq + p^2$$

and that the terms of Table 2.2 are the expansion of

$$(q + p)^3 = q^3 + 3q^2p + 3qp^2 + p^3$$

We conclude therefore that the probabilities of obtaining 0, 1, 2, 3 ... defectives in a sample of n items are given by the successive terms of the expansion of $(q + p)^n$ (see Table 3.3).

Table 3.3

Number of defectives	Probability
0	q^n
1	$nq^{n-1}p$
2	$\dfrac{n(n-1)}{2!}q^{n-2}p^2$
3	$\dfrac{n(n-1)(n-2)}{3!}q^{n-3}p^3$
4	$\dfrac{n(n-)(n-2)(n-3)}{4!}q^{n-4}p^4$

In using Table 3.3 it must be clearly understood that

n = the number of items in the sample

p = the probability of finding a defective item in a single trial

q = the probability of finding a good item in a single trial

The work in calculating the numerical coefficients may become tedious and they may be obtained from Pascal's triangle which is shown in Fig. 3.3.

Each number in the triangle is obtained from the line immediately above by adding together the two numbers which lie on either side of it. Thus in the line $n = 6$ the number 20 is obtained by adding together the numbers 10 and 10 in the line $n = 5$. Also, in the line $n = 8$ the number 28 is obtained by adding the numbers 21 and 7 in the line $n = 7$.

The expansion of $(q + p)^n$ is easily obtained if we remember that the powers of q decrease successively from q^n (which is the first term always) whilst the powers of p increase to p^n (which is always the last term). Thus:

$$(q + p)^5 = q^5 + 5q^4p + 10q^3p^2 + 10q^2p^3 + 5qp^4 + p^5$$
$$(q + p)^7 = q^7 + 7q^6p + 21q^5p^2 + 35q^4p^3 + 35q^3p^4 + 21q^2p^5 + 7qp^6 + p^7$$

Alternatively the binomial coefficients can be found by using Table 3.4.

Value of n	Numerical coefficients in expansion of $(p + q)^n$
	1
1	1 1
2	1 2 1
3	1 3 3 1
4	1 4 6 4 1
5	1 5 10 10 5 1
6	1 6 15 20 15 6 1
7	1 7 21 35 35 21 7 1
8	1 8 28 56 70 56 28 8 1

Fig. 3.3.   Pascal's triangle

Table 3.4   Binomial Coefficients

$r:$	0	1	2	3	4	5	6	7	8	9	10
$n =$											
1	1	1									
2	1	2	1								
3	1	3	3	1							
4	1	4	6	4	1						
5	1	5	10	10	5	1					
6	1	6	15	20	15	6	1				
7	1	7	21	35	35	21	7	1			
8	1	8	28	56	70	56	28	8	1		
9	1	9	36	84	126	126	84	36	9	1	
10	1	10	45	120	210	252	210	120	45	10	1
11	1	11	55	165	330	462	462	330	165	55	11
12	1	12	66	220	495	792	924	792	495	220	66
13	1	13	78	286	715	1287	1716	1716	1287	715	286
14	1	14	91	364	1001	2002	3003	3432	3003	2002	1001
15	1	15	105	455	1365	3003	5005	6435	6435	5005	3003
16	1	16	120	560	1820	4368	8008	11440	12870	11440	8008
17	1	17	136	680	2380	6188	12376	19448	24310	24310	19448
18	1	18	153	816	3060	8568	18564	31824	43758	48620	43758
19	1	19	171	969	3876	11628	27132	50388	75582	92378	92378
20	1	20	190	1140	4845	15504	38760	77520	125970	167960	184756

WHEN TO USE THE BINOMIAL THEOREM

The Binomial Theorem may be used whenever a series of trials satisfies the following conditions:

(a) There are only two possible outcomes in each trial which are mutually exclusive. These outcomes may be success and failure, defective and non-defective, go or not go, etc.

(b) The probability of success in each trial is constant. The probability of success is usually denoted by p and the probability of failure is usually denoted by $q = 1 - p$.

(c) The outcomes of successive trials are mutually independent. This condition is met approximately when items are selected from a large batch and classified as defective and non-defective.

EXAMPLE 1

It is known that 10% of the resistors produced by a certain process are defective. From a large batch a sample of 5 resistors is taken at random. Find the probabilities of obtaining 0, 1, 2, 3, 4 and 5 defective resistors in the sample and draw a histogram to represent these probabilities.

The probability of a single resistor, chosen at random, being defective is $p = \dfrac{10}{100} = 0.1$.

The probability of it being good is $q = 1 - p = 0.9$.

The number in the sample is $n = 5$.

Now

$$(q + p)^5 = q^5 + 5q^4p + 10q^3p^2 + 10q^2p^3 + 5qp^4 + p^5$$

The probabilities are shown in the table below and the histogram is drawn in Fig. 3.4.

Number of defectives in the sample	Term of expansion	Probability	
0	q^5	$(0.9)^5$	$= 0.590\,49$
1	$5q^4p$	$5 \times (0.9)^4 \times (0.1)$	$= 0.328\,05$
2	$10q^3p^2$	$10 \times (0.9)^3 \times (0.1)^2$	$= 0.072\,90$
3	$10q^2p^3$	$10 \times (0.9)^2 \times (0.1)^3$	$= 0.008\,10$
4	$5qp^4$	$5 \times (0.9) \times (0.1)^4$	$= 0.000\,45$
5	p^5	$(0.1)^5$	$= 0.000\,01$
Total probability covering all possible events			$= 1.000\,00$

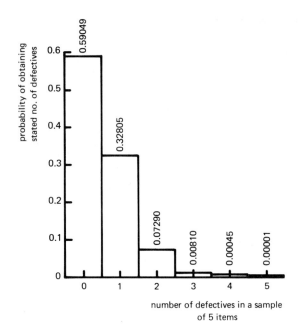

probability of obtaining
stated no. of defectives

number of defectives in a sample
of 5 items

Fig. 3.4

EXAMPLE 2

Cartons which contain 4 items each are checked and it is found that 8%
of the items are defective. If 10 000 cartons are purchased find:

(a) How many cartons are expected to have no defective items.
(b) How many cartons are expected to have 1 defective item.
(c) How many cartons are expected to have less than 2 defective items.
(d) How many defective items there are likely to be in the 10 000 cartons.

(a) If one carton is selected at random then the probability of it containing no defective items is given by the first term of $(q + p)^4$ which is
q^4. Since $p = 0.08$, then $q = 0.92$ and $q^4 = (0.92)^4 = 0.716\,4$
the number of cartons containing no defective items is expected to be
$0.716\,4 \times 10\,000 = 7\,164$.

(b) The probability of finding a carton with 1 defective item in it is the
second term of $(q + p)^4$, i.e. $4q^3p = 4 \times (0.92)^3 \times 0.08 = 0.249\,2$.
The number of cartons with 1 defective item is expected to be
$0.249\,2 \times 10\,000 = 2\,492$.

(c) The number of cartons containing less than 2 defective items (i.e.
containing no defective items or containing 1 defective item) is
expected to be $7\,164 + 2\,492 = 9\,656$.

(d) The number of defective items in the 10 000 boxes is expected to be
$4 \times 10\,000 \times 0.08 = 3\,200$.

THE BINOMIAL DISTRIBUTION

A distribution formed by using the binomial theorem is called a binomial distribution.

EXAMPLE 3

A machine is known to produce 10% of defective parts. Samples of 4 items are taken from the batches produced and examined. If 1000 samples are checked draw a histogram showing the number of defectives which are to be expected.

Here $p = 0.1$, $q = 1 - p = 0.9$ and $n = 4$.

$$(q + p)^4 = q^4 + 4q^3p + 6q^2p^2 + 4qp^3 + p^4$$

The distribution is shown in the table below:

Number of defectives per sample	Term of the binomial expansion	Probability of the stated number of defectives being found in the sample	Number of samples with the stated number of defectives
0	q^4	$(0.9)^4 = 0.656$	$1000 \times 0.656 = 656$
1	$4q^3p$	$4 \times (0.9)^3 \times (0.1) = 0.292$	$1000 \times 0.292 = 292$
2	$6q^2p^2$	$6 \times (0.9)^2 \times (0.1)^2 = 0.049$	$1000 \times 0.049 = 49$
3	$4qp^3$	$4 \times (0.9) \times (0.1)^3 = 0.003$	$1000 \times 0.003 = 3$
4	p^4	$(0.1)^4 = 0.000$	0

Fig. 3.5 shows the histogram representing the distribution.

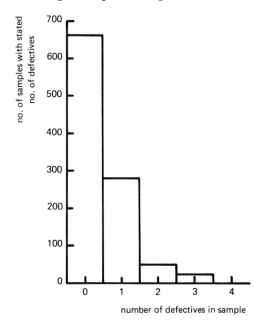

Fig. 3.5

EXAMPLE 4

8 coins are tossed together 256 times. Draw up a theoretical frequency table for the number of heads which may be expected and hence construct a histogram to represent the theoretical frequency distribution.

Here $p = \dfrac{1}{2}$, $q = \dfrac{1}{2}$ and $n = 8$.

$$(q + p)^8 = q^8 + 8q^7p + 28q^6p^2 + 56q^5p^3 + 70q^4p^4$$
$$+ 56q^3p^5 + 28q^2p^6 + 8qp^7 + p^8$$

The theoretical frequencies are calculated in the table on page 47 and the histogram of the theoretical frequency distribution is shown in Fig. 3.6.

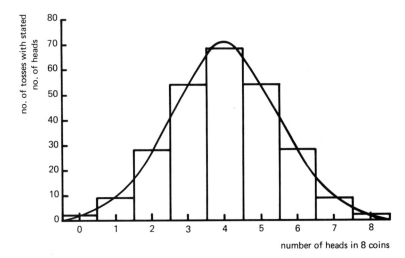

Fig. 3.6

On comparing Figs. 3.5 and 3.6 we see that the histogram of Fig. 3.5 is skewed to the right whilst that of Fig. 3.6 is symmetrical. A histogram of a binomial distribution is symmetrical if, and only if, $p = q = \dfrac{1}{2}$. However when np is greater than 5 the histogram is reasonably symmetrical, but for values of np less than 5 the histogram will be noticeably skewed.

EXAMPLE 5

It is known that a certain process produces 10% of defective articles. If a sample of 20 items is taken at random from a large batch of articles, find the probability of the sample containing 2 or more defective items.

Number of heads in the 8 coins	Term of the binomial expansion	Probability of the stated number of heads occurring	Number of tosses with the stated number of heads
0	q^8	$\left(\dfrac{1}{2}\right)^8 \quad = \quad \dfrac{1}{2^8}$	$\dfrac{1}{2^8} \times 2^8 = 1$
1	$8q^7p$	$8 \times \left(\dfrac{1}{2}\right)^7\left(\dfrac{1}{2}\right) = 8 \times \dfrac{1}{2^8}$	$8 \times \dfrac{1}{2^8} \times 2^8 = 8$
2	$28q^6p^2$	$28 \times \left(\dfrac{1}{2}\right)^6\left(\dfrac{1}{2}\right)^2 = 28 \times \dfrac{1}{2^8}$	$28 \times \dfrac{1}{2^8} \times 2^8 = 28$
3	$56q^5p^3$	$56 \times \left(\dfrac{1}{2}\right)^5\left(\dfrac{1}{2}\right)^3 = 56 \times \dfrac{1}{2^8}$	$56 \times \dfrac{1}{2^8} \times 2^8 = 56$
4	$70q^4p^4$	$70 \times \left(\dfrac{1}{2}\right)^4\left(\dfrac{1}{2}\right)^4 = 70 \times \dfrac{1}{2^8}$	$70 \times \dfrac{1}{2^8} \times 2^8 = 70$
5	$56q^3p^5$	$56 \times \left(\dfrac{1}{2}\right)^3\left(\dfrac{1}{2}\right)^5 = 56 \times \dfrac{1}{2^8}$	$56 \times \dfrac{1}{2^8} \times 2^8 = 56$
6	$28q^2p^6$	$28 \times \left(\dfrac{1}{2}\right)^2\left(\dfrac{1}{2}\right)^6 = 28 \times \dfrac{1}{2^8}$	$28 \times \dfrac{1}{2^8} \times 2^8 = 28$
7	$8qp^7$	$8 \times \left(\dfrac{1}{2}\right)\left(\dfrac{1}{2}\right)^7 = 8 \times \dfrac{1}{2^8}$	$8 \times \dfrac{1}{2^8} \times 2^8 = 8$
8	p^8	$\left(\dfrac{1}{2}\right)^8 \quad = \quad \dfrac{1}{2^8}$	$\dfrac{1}{2^8} \times 2^8 = 1$

Here $p = 0.1$ and $q = 0.9$. Since $n = 20$ we require the first two terms of the expansion of $(q + p)^{20}$.

Number of defective items in the sample	Term of the expansion	Probability of obtaining the stated number of defective items in the sample
0	q	$(0.9)^{20} \qquad\qquad = 0.1216$
1	$20q^{19}p$	$20 \times (0.9)^{19} \times (0.1) = 0.2702$

$$\text{Pr(less than 2)} = \text{Pr(0)} + \text{Pr(1)} = 0.1216 + 0.2702 = 0.3918$$

$$\text{Pr(2 or more)} = 1 - \text{Pr(less than 2)} = 1 - 0.3918 = 0.6082$$

(Since the total probability covering all possible events is 1.)

THE MEAN AND STANDARD DEVIATION OF A
BINOMIAL DISTRIBUTION

It can be proved that the mean and standard deviation for a binomial distribution are given by:

$$\bar{x} = np \quad \text{and} \quad \sigma = \sqrt{npq}$$

EXAMPLE 6

A production process is 6% defective. From a large batch a sample of 200 items is taken. Calculate the mean number of defectives in the sample and the standard deviation.

$$\bar{x} = np = 200 \times 0.06 = 12$$
$$\sigma = \sqrt{npq} = \sqrt{200 \times 0.06 \times 0.94} = 3.36$$

EXERCISE 4

1) 5% of the fuses produced by a production process are known to be defective. A sample of 4 fuses is taken from a large batch. Find the probabilities of the sample containing 0, 1, 2, 3 and 4 defective fuses.

2) Electric light bulbs are packed in boxes containing 100 bulbs. If the production process produces 2% of defective bulbs find the probability of a box containing 2 or more defective bulbs.

3) A firm purchases 5000 boxes of resistors each of which contains 5 resistors. A sample of boxes is checked and it is found that 4% of the resistors are defective. Find:

(a) How many boxes are likely to contain 0 defective resistors.
(b) How many boxes are likely to contain 1 defective resistor.
(c) How many defective items there are likely to be in the 5000 boxes.

4) A machine produces 10% of defective items. Samples of 5 items are taken from the batches produced and examined. If 2000 samples are checked, calculate the number of samples expected to contain 0 defective items, 1 defective item, 2, 3, 4 and 5 defective items. Draw a histogram to show the distribution of defective items.

5) 3% of the components produced on a certain machine are defective. Find the probability that in a sample of 50 components:

(a) 0 will be defective,
(b) 1 will be defective,
(c) 1 or less will be defective,
(d) 2 or more will be defective.

6) 22% of the telephone calls coming into a certain switchboard last 5 minutes or less. In 20 successive calls find the probability that 2 or more will last more than 5 minutes.

7) A product is being made in large quantities. Successive samples of 50

items gave the following numbers of defective items: 2, 2, 0, 0, 1, 3, 0, 2, 0 and 0. Find:

(a) The percentage defective.
(b) The mean number of defective items produced per sample and the standard deviation.
(c) The probability of a sample containing one or more defective items in it.

8) 1% of electronic components are known to be defective. If these are packed in boxes containing 300 components determine:

(a) The average (mean) number of defective items in a box.
(b) The standard deviation.
(c) The probability of a box containing exactly 3 defective items.
(d) The probability of a box containing 3 or more defective items.

Chapter 4

The Poisson Distribution

After reaching the end of this chapter you should be able to:

1) Describe the Poisson situation.

2) Define the Poisson distribution and calculate probabilities using tables of e^{-x} and tables of cumulative probabilities.

3) State and use the formula for the mean and standard deviation of a Poisson distribution.

4) Describe the conditions under which the Poisson distribution can be used as an approximation to the binomial distribution and use it as such.

5) Solve problems using the cumulation of terms of the Poisson distribution.

THE POISSON DISTRIBUTION

There exists a series for e^{λ} which is:

$$e^{\lambda} = 1 + \lambda + \frac{\lambda^2}{2!} + \frac{\lambda^3}{3!} + \ldots$$

where e is the base of natural logarithms. The value of e is 2.7183 correct to four places of decimals.

In any calculation involving probabilities, the total probability covering all possible events must be equal to 1.

Now
$$e^{\lambda} \times e^{-\lambda} = e^{0} = 1$$

Hence we can use the product $e^{\lambda} \cdot e^{-\lambda}$ to form a theoretical frequency distribution when it is written in the form:

$$e^{-\lambda}\left(1 + \lambda + \frac{\lambda^2}{2!} + \frac{\lambda^3}{3!} + \ldots\right)$$

A distribution obtained by using this series is called a Poisson distribution. Tables of values of e^{-x} are available in most books of Mathematical Tables.

RELATION BETWEEN THE POISSON AND BINOMIAL DISTRIBUTIONS

In the binomial distribution if n (the number of items in a sample) is large and p (the fraction defective) is small then the event of finding a defective item in the sample is called a *rare event*.

In practice if $n \geqslant 50$ and $np < 5$ the event may be considered rare. In such cases the Poisson distribution gives a very close approximation to the binomial distribution.

Generally the approximation between a binomial and Poisson distribution is good if $p \leqslant 0.1$ and $np \leqslant 5$.

USING THE POISSON DISTRIBUTION AS AN APPROXIMATION TO THE BINOMIAL DISTRIBUTION

In the majority of engineering processes the fraction defective, p, is usually small. If we take a sample of n items from a batch of such items, the expected number of defectives in the sample will be $\lambda = np$. Hence the Poisson distribution may be used as an approximation to the binomial distribution if λ represents the expected number of defectives in a sample of n items. Thus:

the probability of obtaining 0 defectives $= \Pr(0) = e^{-\lambda} \times 1 = e^{-\lambda}$

the probability of obtaining 1 defectives $= \Pr(1) = e^{-\lambda} \times \lambda = \lambda e^{-\lambda}$

the probability of obtaining 2 defectives $= \Pr(2) = e^{-\lambda} \times \dfrac{\lambda^2}{2!} = \dfrac{\lambda^2}{2!} e^{-\lambda}$

the probability of obtaining 3 defectives $= \Pr(3) = e^{-\lambda} \times \dfrac{\lambda^3}{3!} = \dfrac{\lambda^3}{3!} e^{-\lambda}$

etc.

In calculating the above Poisson probabilities the following 'short cut' method may be used.

$$\Pr(0) = e^{-\lambda}$$

$$\Pr(1) = \lambda \Pr(0)$$

$$\Pr(2) = \frac{\lambda}{2} \Pr(1)$$

$$\Pr(3) = \frac{\lambda}{3} \Pr(2) \quad \text{etc.}$$

EXAMPLE 1

A process is known to produce 2% of defective items. A sample of 100 items is drawn at random from a large batch of these items. Find the probabilities of obtaining 0, 1, 2 and 3 defective items in the sample.

Here $p = 0.02$ and $n = 100$.

Hence $$\lambda = np = 100 \times 0.02 = 2$$

From the Table of e^{-x}, $e^{-2} = 0.135\,3$.

Number of defective items in the sample	Probability of obtaining the stated number of defective items in the sample
0	$\Pr(0) = e^{-\lambda} \quad = 0.135\,3$
1	$\Pr(1) = \lambda e^{-\lambda} = \lambda\,\Pr(0) = 2 \times 0.135\,3 = 0.270\,6$
2	$\Pr(2) = \dfrac{\lambda^2}{2!} e^{-\lambda} = \dfrac{\lambda}{2}\Pr(1) = \dfrac{2}{2} \times 0.270\,6 = 0.270\,6$
3	$\Pr(3) = \dfrac{\lambda^3}{3!} e^{-\lambda} = \dfrac{\lambda}{3}\Pr(2) = \dfrac{2}{3} \times 0.270\,6 = 0.180\,4$

EXAMPLE 2

It is known that a certain process produces 8% of defective items. A sample of 50 items is drawn from a large batch produced by the process. Find the probabilities of finding 0, 1 and 2 defective items in the sample by using:

(a) the Poisson distribution,
(b) the binomial distribution.

(a) For the Poisson distribution $p = 0.08$ and $n = 50$.

$$\therefore \qquad \lambda = np = 50 \times 0.08 = 4$$

$$e^{-\lambda} = e^{-4} = 0.018\,3$$

(b) For the binomial distribution $p = 0.08$, $q = 0.92$ and $n = 50$.

$$(q + p)^{50} = q^{50} + 50q^{49}p + \frac{50 \times 49}{2!}q^{48}p^2 \dots$$

$$= q^{50} + 50q^{49}p + 1225q^{48}p^2 \dots$$

Number of defective items in the sample	Probability	
	Poisson	Binomial
0	$e^{-\lambda} = 0.018\,3$	$q^{50} = (0.92)^{50} = 0.015\,5$
1	$\lambda e^{-\lambda} = 0.073\,2$	$50q^{49}p = 0.067\,2$
2	$\dfrac{\lambda^2}{2!} e^{-\lambda} = 0.146\,4$	$1225q^{48}p^2 = 0.143\,3$

On comparing the probabilities as calculated for both the Poisson and binomial distributions it will be seen that the Poisson distribution is a reasonable approximation to the binomial distribution.

EXAMPLE 3

A process produces 3% of defective articles. From a large batch of these articles a sample of 80 items is taken. Find the probability that the sample will contain 2 or more defective items.

Here $p = 0.03$ and $n = 80$.

Hence
$$\lambda = np = 80 \times 0.03 = 2.4$$
$$e^{-\lambda} = e^{-2.4} = 0.090\,7$$

Number of defective articles in the sample	Probability
0	$\Pr(0) = e^{-\lambda} = 0.090\,7$
1	$\Pr(1) = \lambda\,\Pr(0) = 0.217\,7$

Probability of 1 or less defective items in the sample

$$= 0.090\,7 + 0.217\,7 = 0.308\,4$$

Hence probability of 2 or more defective items in the sample

$$= 1 - 0.308\,4 = 0.691\,6$$

TABLES OF POISSON PROBABILITIES

Tables of Poisson probabilities are available (see, for instance, *Tables, Data and Formulae for Engineers* published by Stanley Thornes (Publishers) Ltd.) Part of such a table is reproduced below.

Poisson Distribution

X	2.1	2.2	2.3	2.4	2.5	λ 2.6	2.7	2.8	2.9	3.0
0	0.122 5	0.110 8	0.100 3	0.090 7	0.082 1	0.074 3	0.067 2	0.060 8	0.055 0	0.049 8
1	0.257 2	0.243 8	0.230 6	0.217 7	0.205 2	0.193 1	0.181 5	0.170 3	0.159 6	0.149 4
2	0.270 0	0.268 1	0.265 2	0.261 3	0.256 5	0.251 0	0.245 0	0.238 4	0.231 4	0.224 0
3	0.189 0	0.196 6	0.203 3	0.209 0	0.213 8	0.217 6	0.220 5	0.222 5	0.223 7	0.224 0
4	0.099 2	0.108 2	0.116 9	0.125 4	0.133 6	0.141 4	0.148 8	0.155 7	0.162 2	0.168 0
5	0.041 7	0.047 6	0.053 8	0.060 2	0.066 8	0.073 5	0.080 4	0.087 2	0.094 0	0.100 8
6	0.014 6	0.017 4	0.020 6	0.024 1	0.027 8	0.031 9	0.036 2	0.040 7	0.045 5	0.050 4
7	0.004 4	0.005 5	0.006 8	0.008 3	0.009 9	0.011 8	0.013 9	0.016 3	0.018 8	0.021 6
8	0.001 1	0.001 5	0.001 9	0.002 5	0.003 1	0.003 8	0.004 7	0.005 7	0.006 8	0.008 1
9	0.000 3	0.000 4	0.000 5	0.000 7	0.000 9	0.001 1	0.001 4	0.001 8	0.002 2	0.002 7
10	0.000 1	0.000 1	0.000 1	0.000 2	0.000 2	0.000 3	0.000 4	0.000 5	0.000 6	0.000 8
11	0.000 0	0.000 0	0.000 0	0.000 0	0.000 0	0.000 1	0.000 1	0.000 1	0.000 2	0.000 2
12	0.000 0	0.000 0	0.000 0	0.000 0	0.000 0	0.000 0	0.000 0	0.000 0	0.000 0	0.000 1

Entries in the table give the probabilities that an event will occur x times when the average number of occurrences is λ.

From the table above, when $\lambda = 2.4$:

$$\text{Pr}(0 \text{ defective articles}) = 0.090\,7$$
$$\text{Pr}(1 \text{ defective article}) = 0.217\,7$$

which agree with the values calculated in Example 3.

THE POISSON DISTRIBUTION IN ITS OWN RIGHT

We have seen that the Poisson distribution may be used as an approximation to the binomial distribution provided certain conditions are met. To do this we must know the values of n (the sample size) and p (the fraction defective) in the expression $(q + p)^n$.

There are, however, very many cases where the value of n is not known. For instance, in checking the number of weaving defects in a length of cloth or the number of welding defects in a welded assembly. In these cases we may use the Poisson distribution to determine probabilities provided that λ is made equal to the average value of the occurrence of the event.

EXAMPLE 4

By checking several cartons containing large numbers of bolts it was found that the average number of defective bolts a carton was 2. Find the probability of finding a box containing 3 or more defective bolts.

Here $\lambda = 2$ and $e^{-\lambda} = 0.135\,3$.

Number of defective bolts in a carton	Probability
0	$\text{Pr}(0) = e^{-\lambda} \qquad = 0.135\,3$
1	$\text{Pr}(1) = \lambda\,\text{Pr}(0) = 0.270\,7$
2	$\text{Pr}(2) = \dfrac{\lambda}{2}\,\text{Pr}(1) = 0.270\,7$

Probability of 2 or less defective bolts in a carton

$$= 0.135\,3 + 0.270\,7 + 0.270\,7 = 0.676\,7$$

Hence the probability of 3 or more defective bolts in a carton

$$= 1 - 0.676\,7 = 0.323\,3$$

It is likely, therefore, that 32.33% of all the cartons will contain 3 or more defective bolts.

EXAMPLE 5

20 sheets of aluminium alloy were examined for surface flaws. The number of flaws per sheet were as follows:

Sheet number	0	1	2	3	4	5	6	7	8	9	10	11	12
Number of flaws	4	0	2	6	4	2	0	0	2	0	4	4	2

Sheet number	13	14	15	16	17	18	19	20
Number of flaws	1	3	4	1	1	5	3	2

Find the probability of finding a sheet, chosen at random from a batch of these sheets, which contains 3 or more surface flaws.

$$\lambda = \text{the average number of flaws per sheet} = \frac{\text{total number of flaws}}{\text{number of sheets checked}}$$

$$= \frac{50}{20} = 2.5$$

$$e^{-\lambda} = e^{-2.5} = 0.082\,1$$

Number of flaws per sheet	Probability
0	$\Pr(0) = e^{-\lambda} \qquad = 0.082\,1$
1	$\Pr(1) = \lambda\,\Pr(0) = 0.205\,2$
2	$\Pr(2) = \dfrac{\lambda}{2}\,\Pr(1) = 0.256\,5$

Probability of finding a sheet with 3 or more surface flaws

$$= 1 - (0.082\,1 + 0.205\,2 + 0.256\,5) = 0.456\,2$$

Hence it is likely that 45.62% of the sheets in the batch will contain 3 or more surface flaws.

THE MEAN AND STANDARD DEVIATION OF A POISSON DISTRIBUTION

It can be shown that the mean and standard deviation of a Poisson distribution are

$$\bar{x} = \lambda \quad \text{and} \quad \sigma = \sqrt{\lambda}$$

EXAMPLE 6

The table over shows the frequency of accidents in a factory during a 100 day period. Calculate the mean and standard deviation for this distribution. Show that the distribution is well represented by a Poisson distribution with $\bar{x} = \lambda$ and $\sigma = \sqrt{\lambda}$.

Number of accidents	0	1	2	3	4
Number of days on which this number of accidents occurred	42	36	14	6	2

Number of accidents $= x$	Frequency $= f$	fx	fx^2
0	42	0	0
1	36	36	36
2	14	28	56
3	6	18	54
4	2	8	32
	100	90	178

$$\bar{x} = \frac{90}{100} = 0.9$$

$$\sigma = \sqrt{\frac{178}{100} - (0.9)^2} = 0.985$$

Taking $\lambda = 0.9, \quad e^{-\lambda} = 0.406\,6$

Number of accidents	Probability	Expected number of days = probability × 100
0	$\Pr(0) = e^{-\lambda} = 0.406\,6$	40.66 or 41
1	$\Pr(1) = \lambda \Pr(0) = 0.365\,9$	36.59 or 37
2	$\Pr(2) = \dfrac{\lambda}{2} \Pr(1) = 0.164\,7$	16.47 or 16
3	$\Pr(3) = \dfrac{\lambda}{3} \Pr(2) = 0.049\,4$	4.94 or 5
4	$\Pr(4) = \dfrac{\lambda}{4} \Pr(3) = 0.011\,1$	1.11 or 1

Hence the given distribution is well represented by a Poisson distribution with $\lambda = 0.9$. The standard deviation of the Poisson distribution is:

$$\sigma = \sqrt{\lambda} = \sqrt{0.9} = 0.949$$

which agrees very well with the value calculated previously.

EXERCISE 5

1) It is known that 10% of the articles produced on a certain machine

are defective. Using:

(a) the binomial distribution,
(b) the Poisson distribution.

Calculate the probabilities of a sample of 5 items containing 0, 1, 2, 3, 4 and 5 defective items in it.

2) A product is being made in large quantities. Successive samples of 80 items gave the following numbers of defective items: 2, 2, 0, 0, 1, 3, 0, 2, 0 and 0. Estimate the probabilities, using Poisson, of finding a sample of 80 items with:

(a) 0 defective items in it,
(b) 1 defective item in it,
(c) 2 defective items in it,
(d) 3 or more defective items in it.

3) 1% of fuses produced at a certain factory are known to be defective. If these are packed in boxes containing 250 find the probabilities that a box will contain:

(a) exactly 3 defective fuses,
(b) 3 or more defective fuses.

4) Show that the following distribution approximately conforms to a Poisson distribution.

Number of weaving defects per piece of cloth	0	1	2	3	4	5
Frequency of pieces	30	52	50	30	16	6

Calculate the standard deviation for the given distribution and compare its value with that for the Poisson distribution.

5) The mean number of calls per hour received on a switchboard is 4. Using Poisson, determine the probability that in a particular hour 4 calls are received.

6) In a large consignment of components packed in bags, it was found that the average number of defective components per bag was 3. Find the probability of finding a bag with 2 or more defective components in it.

7) 10 sheets of plastic were examined for flaws. The number of flaws per sheet were:

Sheet number	1	2	3	4	5	6	7	8	9	10
Number of flaws	3	2	2	1	0	1	3	1	1	1

Calculate the percentage of sheets which are likely to have 2 or more flaws.

8) 500 samples of the same size were taken from a production process.

The number of defective items in the samples were as follows:

Number of defective items	0	1	2	3	4	5
Number of samples containing this number of defective items	215	191	75	17	2	0

Show that this distribution is approximately represented by a Poisson distribution with $\bar{x} = \lambda$. Calculate the standard deviation of the given distribution and compare it with that for the Poisson distribution.

9) A sampling apparatus collects a one litre sample of the atmosphere in a certain mine and counts the number of dust particles in it. After collecting several samples it is found that the mean number of dust particles per litre is 5. What is the probability of collecting a litre sample with less than 2 dust particles in it.

10) An electronic component is mass produced and then checked on an automatic testing machine which classifies it as good or defective. The batch contains 10% of defective items. If the components are checked in batches of 10, find the probability that a sample will contain 2 or more defective components.

Chapter 5

The Normal Distribution

After reaching the end of this chapter you should be able to:

1) Calculate the probabilities for normal distributions with mean zero and standard deviation of unity, using normal distribution tables.

2) Convert data from a general normal distribution to standardised form.

3) Solve problems concerning the normal distribution using (2) and tables.

4) Plot relative frequency percentages against the variate on normal probability paper.

5) Determine whether the points lie on a straight line in (4).

6) Determine the mean and standard deviation using normal probability paper.

INTRODUCTION

The three histograms shown in Figs. 1.1, 1.2 and 1.3 (pages 3, 4 and 6) all exhibit the same tendency in that most of the values are grouped near the centre of the diagram with a few values more widely dispersed. If we draw frequency curves to represent the three distributions we obtain, approximately, the bell-shaped curve shown in Fig. 5.1. This curve is known as the normal distribution curve and many distributions obtained by measuring follow it closely.

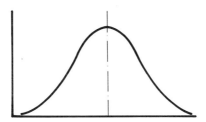

Fig. 5.1.   The normal curve

PROBABILITY FROM THE NORMAL CURVE

The normal curve can be defined mathematically in terms of the arithmetic mean and the standard deviation. Since the normal curve is symmetrical about its centre-line, the centre-line represents the mean of the distribution.

The arithmetic mean locates the mean position of the curve from the reference axis as shown in Fig 5.2 which displays similar distributions but with different means.

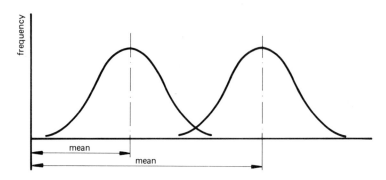

Fig. 5.2.   Two similar distributions but with different means

The standard deviation gives a measure of the spread (or dispersion) of the curve about the mean. As shown in Fig. 5.3 the standard deviation is the distance from the mean to the points of inflexion of the curve. Although the normal curve extends to infinity on either side of the mean, for most practical purposes it may be assumed to terminate at three standard deviations on either side of the mean.

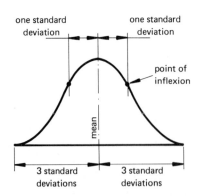

Fig. 5.3.   The standard deviation is a measure of the spread or dispersion of the normal curve

Since the total probability is equal to unity, if we make the area under the normal curve equal to 1, then we can use the areas under the curve to estimate probabilities. For convenience, the origin is taken at the intersection of the mean and the horizontal axis (Fig. 5.4). The horizontal axis

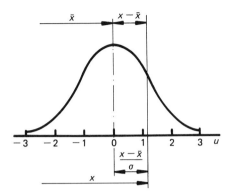

Fig. 5.4

is then marked off in units of the standard deviation. Any deviation from the mean can then be calculated by using:

$$u = \frac{x - \bar{x}}{\sigma} \quad \text{where } x = \text{value of the variate}$$

$$\bar{x} = \text{mean}$$

$$\text{and } \sigma = \text{standard deviation}$$

EXAMPLE 1

For a certain process it was found that $\bar{x} = 15.00\,\text{mm}$ and $\sigma = 0.30\,\text{mm}$. Express the dimensions:

(a) 14.70 mm (b) 15.21 mm

in terms of the standard deviation.

(a) Here $x = 14.70\,\text{mm}$ and $u = \dfrac{14.70 - 15.00}{0.30} = -1.$

Hence the dimension 14.70 mm lies 1 standard deviation below the mean.

(b) Here $x = 15.21\,\text{mm}$ and $u = \dfrac{15.21 - 15.00}{0.30} = 0.7.$

Hence the dimension 15.21 mm lies 0.7 standard deviations above the mean.

The shaded area (Fig. 5.5) gives the probability of something occurring between the mean value $(u = 0)$ and 1.5 standard deviations from the mean $(u = 1.5)$.

In practice areas under the normal curve (and hence probabilities) are found by using Table 5.1. Notice that since the normal curve is symmetrical about its centre-line the area of each half is 0.5.

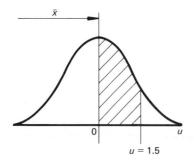

Fig. 5.5

USING THE TABLE OF AREAS UNDER THE NORMAL CURVE

Fig. 5.5 shows a typical area. To use Table 5.1 note that the figures in the first column are values of u in increments of 0.1. The corresponding value in the column headed 0 gives the area between $u = 0$ and the value of u in the first column. Thus the area between $u = 0$ and $u = 1.5$ is 0.433 2.

If the value of u has two decimal places the area will be found in the appropriate column of the next nine columns. Thus the area between $u = 0$ and $u = 1.53$ is 0.437 0.

When the value of u is negative the table is used in exactly the same way, the negative sign being ignored when finding an area.

The following examples show how areas under the normal curve are found in practice.

EXAMPLES 2

1) Find the area under the normal curve between $t = 0$ and $u = 0.78$ (Fig. 5.6).

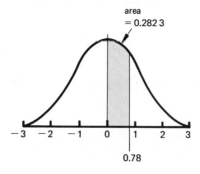

Fig. 5.6

The area is found directly from Table 5.1 as 0.282 3.

Table 5.1   Areas under the Standard Normal Curve from 0 to *u*

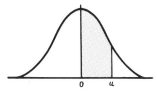

u	0	1	2	3	4	5	6	7	8	9
0.0	.000 0	.004 0	.008 0	.012 0	.016 0	.019 9	.023 9	.027 9	.031 9	.035 9
0.1	.039 8	.043 8	.047 8	.051 7	.055 7	.059 6	.063 6	.067 5	.071 4	.075 4
0.2	.079 3	.083 2	.087 1	.091 0	.094 8	.098 7	.102 6	.106 4	.110 3	.114 1
0.3	.117 9	.121 7	.125 5	.129 3	.133 1	.136 8	.140 6	.144 3	.148 0	.151 7
0.4	.155 4	.159 1	.162 8	.166 4	.170 0	.173 6	.177 2	.180 8	.184 4	.187 9
0.5	.191 5	.195 0	.198 5	.201 9	.205 4	.208 8	.212 3	.215 7	.219 0	.222 4
0.6	.225 8	.229 1	.232 4	.235 7	.238 9	.242 2	.245 4	.248 6	.251 8	.254 9
0.7	.258 0	.261 2	.264 2	.267 3	.270 4	.273 4	.276 4	.279 4	.282 3	.285 2
0.8	.288 1	.291 0	.293 9	.296 7	.299 6	.302 3	.305 1	.307 8	.310 6	.313 3
0.9	.315 9	.318 6	.321 2	.323 8	.326 4	.328 9	.331 5	.334 0	.336 5	.338 9
1.0	.341 3	.343 8	.346 1	.348 5	.350 8	.353 1	.355 4	.357 7	.359 9	.362 1
1.1	.364 3	.366 5	.368 6	.370 8	.372 9	.374 9	.377 0	.379 0	.381 0	.383 0
1.2	.384 9	.386 9	.388 8	.390 7	.392 5	.394 4	.396 2	.398 0	.399 7	.401 5
1.3	.403 2	.404 9	.406 6	.408 2	.409 9	.411 5	.413 1	.414 7	.416 2	.417 7
1.4	.419 2	.420 7	.422 2	.423 6	.425 1	.426 5	.427 9	.429 2	.430 6	.431 9
1.5	.433 2	.434 5	.435 7	.437 0	.438 2	.439 4	.440 6	.441 8	.442 9	.444 1
1.6	.445 2	.446 3	.447 4	.448 4	.449 5	.450 5	.451 5	.452 5	.453 5	.454 5
1.7	.455 4	.456 4	.457 3	.458 2	.459 1	.459 9	.460 8	.461 6	.462 5	.463 3
1.8	.464 1	.464 9	.465 6	.466 4	.467 1	.467 8	.468 6	.469 3	.469 9	.470 6
1.9	.471 3	.471 9	.472 6	.473 2	.473 8	.474 4	.475 0	.475 6	.476 1	.476 7
2.0	.477 2	.477 8	.478 3	.478 8	.479 3	.479 8	.480 3	.480 8	.481 2	.481 7
2.1	.482 1	.482 6	.483 0	.483 4	.483 8	.484 2	.484 6	.485 0	.485 4	.485 7
2.2	.486 1	.486 4	.486 8	.487 1	.487 5	.487 8	.488 1	.488 4	.488 7	.489 0
2.3	.489 3	.489 6	.489 8	.490 1	.490 4	.490 6	.490 9	.491 1	.491 3	.491 6
2.4	.491 8	.492 0	.492 2	.492 5	.492 7	.492 9	.493 1	.493 2	.493 4	.493 6
2.5	.493 8	.494 0	.494 1	.494 3	.494 5	.494 6	.494 8	.494 9	.495 1	.495 2
2.6	.495 3	.495 5	.495 6	.495 7	.495 9	.496 0	.496 1	.496 2	.496 3	.496 4
2.7	.496 5	.496 6	.496 7	.496 8	.496 9	.497 0	.497 1	.497 2	.497 3	.497 4
2.8	.497 4	.497 5	.497 6	.497 7	.497 7	.497 8	.497 9	.497 9	.498 0	.498 1
2.9	.498 1	.498 2	.498 2	.498 3	.498 4	.498 4	.498 5	.498 5	.498 6	.498 6
3.0	.498 7	.498 7	.498 7	.498 8	.498 8	.498 9	.498 9	.498 9	.499 0	.499 0
3.1	.499 0	.499 1	.499 1	.499 1	.499 2	.499 2	.499 2	.499 2	.499 3	.499 3
3.2	.499 3	.499 3	.499 4	.499 4	.499 4	.499 4	.499 4	.499 5	.499 5	.499 5
3.3	.499 5	.499 5	.499 5	.499 6	.499 6	.499 6	.499 6	.499 6	.499 6	.499 7
3.4	.499 7	.499 7	.499 7	.499 7	.499 7	.499 7	.499 7	.499 7	.499 7	.499 8
3.5	.499 8	.499 8	.499 8	.499 8	.499 8	.499 8	.499 8	.499 8	.499 8	.499 8
3.6	.499 8	.499 8	.499 9	.499 9	.499 9	.499 9	.499 9	.499 9	.499 9	.499 9
3.7	.499 9	.499 9	.499 9	.499 9	.499 9	.499 9	.499 9	.499 9	.499 9	.499 9
3.8	.499 9	.499 9	.499 9	.499 9	.499 9	.499 9	.499 9	.499 9	.499 9	.499 9
3.9	.500 0	.500 0	.500 0	.500 0	.500 0	.500 0	.500 0	.500 0	.500 0	.500 0

2) Find the area under the normal curve between $u = 0$ and $u = -0.88$ (Fig. 5.7).

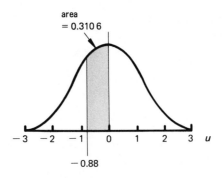

Fig. 5.7

Since the normal curve is symmetrical about the mean we find the required area between $u = 0$ and $u = -0.88$ directly from Table 5.1 as if it was the area between $u = 0$ and $u = 0.88$. Its value is 0.310 6.

3) Find the area under the normal curve between $u = 1.3$ and $u = 1.85$.

First find the area between $u = 0$ and $u = 1.85$. This is 0.467 8. Next find the area between $u = 0$ and $u = 1.3$. This is 0.403 2. The required area is found by subtracting 0.403 2 from 0.467 8 which is 0.064 6 (see Fig. 5.8).

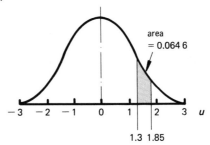

Fig. 5.8

4) Find the area between $u = -0.75$ and $u = 1.26$.

First find the area between $u = 0$ and $u = -0.75$. This is 0.273 4. Next find the area between $u = 0$ and $u = 1.26$. This is 0.396 2. The required area is found by adding the two areas, i.e. $0.273 4 + 0.396 2 = 0.669 6$ (see Fig. 5.9).

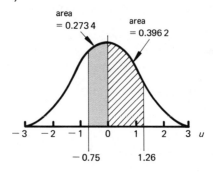

Fig. 5.9

5) Find the tail areas shown in Fig. 5.10.

(a) To find the left hand area first find the area between $u = 0$ and $u = -1.48$ which is $0.430\,6$. Since the area under half the normal curve is 0.5 the tail area is $0.5 - 0.430\,6 = 0.069\,4$.

(b) To find the right hand tail area first find the area between $u = 0$ and $u = 2.05$ which is $0.479\,8$. The tail area is therefore $0.5 - 0.479\,8 = 0.020\,2$.

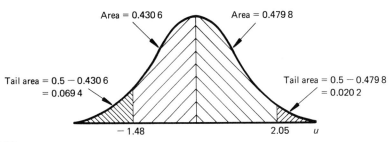

Fig. 5.10

FINDING PROBABILITIES FROM THE NORMAL CURVE

The method is shown in the following example.

EXAMPLE 3

By measuring about 100 parts produced on a lathe it was found that the mean length was 20.05 mm with a standard deviation of 0.02 mm. Find the probability that one component selected at random would have:

(a) a length between 20.03 mm and 20.08 mm;
(b) a length between 20.06 mm and 20.07 mm;
(c) a length less than 20.01 mm;
(d) a length greater than 20.09 mm.

We are given $\bar{x} = 20.05$ mm and $\sigma = 0.02$ mm.

(a) First find the value of u corresponding to $x = 20.03$ mm.

$$u_1 = \frac{x - \bar{x}}{\sigma} = \frac{20.03 - 20.05}{0.02} = -1.00$$

Next find the value of u corresponding to $x = 20.08$ mm.

$$u_2 = \frac{x - \bar{x}}{\sigma} = \frac{20.08 - 20.05}{0.02} = 1.50$$

The probability is given by the area betweeen $u = -1.00$ and $u = 1.50$. Using Table 5.1:

The area between $u = 0$ and $u = -1.00$ is $0.341\,3$.

The area between $u = 0$ and $u = 1.50$ is $0.433\,2$.

Hence the area between $u = -1.00$ and $u = 1.50$ is $0.341\,3 + 0.433\,2 = 0.774\,5$. This is the probability that one component chosen at random would have a length between $20.03\,\text{mm}$ and $20.08\,\text{mm}$. The probability is sometimes expressed as a percentage and it is $0.774\,5 \times 100 = 77.45\%$. *What we are saying is that we expect 77.45% of the parts produced to have a length between 20.03 mm and 20.08 mm.*

(b) When $x = 20.06\,\text{mm}$, $u_1 = \dfrac{20.06 - 20.05}{0.02} = 0.50$.

When $x = 20.07\,\text{mm}$, $u_2 = \dfrac{20.07 - 20.05}{0.02} = 1.00$.

To find the probability we need to find the area between $u = 0.50$ and $u = 1.00$.

Area between $u = 0$ and $u = 1.00$ is $0.341\,3$.

Area between $u = 0$ and $u = 0.50$ is $0.191\,5$.

Area between $u = 0.50$ and $u = 1.00$ is $0.341\,3 - 0.191\,5 = 0.149\,8$.

The probability is therefore $0.149\,8$ or 14.98%. *We expect 14.98% of the parts produced to have a length between 20.06 mm and 20.07 mm.*

(c) When $x = 20.01\,\text{mm}$, $u = \dfrac{20.01 - 20.05}{0.02} = -2.00$.

The diagram (Fig. 5.11) shows that we have to find the left hand tail area.

Area between $u = 0$ and $u = -2.00$ is $0.477\,2$.

The tail area is $0.5 - 0.477\,2 = 0.022\,8$.

The probability is therefore $0.022\,8$ or 2.28%. *That is, we expect 2.28% of the parts produced to have a length less than 20.01 mm.*

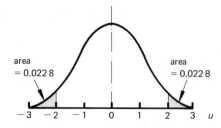

area = 0.022 8

area = 0.022 8

Fig. 5.11

(d) When $x = 20.09\,\text{mm}$, $u = \dfrac{20.09 - 20.05}{0.02} = 2.00$.

From Fig. 5.11 we see that we require the right hand tail area.

Area between $u = 0$ and $u = 2.00$ is 0.477 2.

The tail area is $0.5 - 0.477\,2 = 0.022\,8$.

The probability is therefore 0.022 8 or 2.28% and *we expect 2.28% of the parts to have a length greater than 20.09 mm.*

COMPARISON OF PROCESS LIMITS AND SPECIFICATION LIMITS

The normal curve extends to infinity on either side of the mean but for most practical purposes we may regard it as *terminating at three standard deviations on either side of the mean.*

Every process has an inherent variability and if this variability is too great then defective parts will be produced. The situation whereby these defective parts are produced is shown in Fig. 5.12. When the mean and the standard deviation for the process are known the percentage of defective parts likely to be produced may be calculated as shown in Example 4.

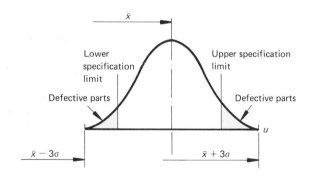

Fig. 5.12

EXAMPLE 4

A process is known to have a mean of 12.51 mm and a standard deviation of 0.015 mm. If the specification limits are 12.50 ± 0.04 mm, what percentage of defectives are likely to be produced?

We are given $\bar{x} = 12.51$ mm and $\sigma = 0.015$ mm. All the parts produced are expected to lie between the limits of $\bar{x} \pm 3\sigma$, that is between 12.51 ± (3 × 0.015) mm or 12.465 mm and 12.555 mm. The situation is then as shown in Fig. 5.13 where it will be seen that defective parts are produced because the upper specification limit is less than $\bar{x} + 3\sigma$.

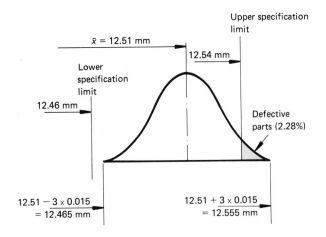

Fig. 5.13

To find the percentage of defectives likely to be produced we must first find the shaded area in Fig. 5.13.

When $x = 12.54\,\text{mm}$, $u = \dfrac{12.54 - 12.51}{0.015} = 2.00.$

From the table of areas under the normal curve (Table 5.1) the area between $u = 0$ and $u = 2.00$ is 0.4772. The shaded area is therefore $0.5 - 0.4772 = 0.0228$. Hence it is expected that the process will produce 2.28% of defective items.

NON-NORMAL FREQUENCY DISTRIBUTION CURVES

It has already been stated that data obtained by measurement should follow the normal curve. This is because all processes have an inherent variability which implies that:

(a) the variations in the process are small;
(b) the variations are likely to occur on either side of the mean (i.e. they are as likely to be positive as negative).

If after plotting an actual frequency distribution we find that the curve is non-normal then the process is not conforming to the two conditions above. Either there is a bias in the process which prevents the variations being just as likely positive or negative or the process contains one or more large variables. Generally the latter cause is the more likely and it is usually not too difficult to trace the causes of the large variations and eliminate them.

Very often the shape of the frequency distribution curve gives the clue as to what has gone wrong. Some examples are given in Fig. 5.14.

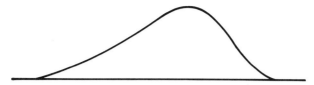

Skewed distribution. Something is causing parts to be produced undersize, for instance, swarf on a stop of a capstan lathe.

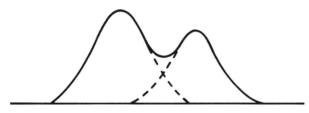

Multi-modal caused by a mixture from two (or more) normal distributions, for instance, from multi-spindle automatic machines. If the humps are the same height then the quantities produced by all the distributions are the same. When the humps are not the same height the quantities produced are different.

Flat topped caused by a setting taking up a number of positions.

Fig. 5.14.   Non-normal frequency distribution curves

CHECKING A DISTRIBUTION TO SEE IF IT IS NORMAL

Arithmetic probability paper may be used to check a distribution to see if it is normal. The method is shown in Example 5.

EXAMPLE 5

The table below shows the distribution of maximum loads supported by a certain make of cable.

Max. load (kN)	84—88	89—93	94—98	99—103	104—108	109—113	114–118	119—123
Frequency	4	10	24	34	28	12	6	2

check if this distribution is normal.

The first step is to convert the given frequency distribution into a percentage cumulative frequency distribution as shown below.

Max load (kN)	Cumulative frequency	% Cumulative frequency
Less than 88.5	4	$\dfrac{4}{120} \times 100 =$ 3.33%
93.5	14	$\dfrac{14}{120} \times 100 =$ 11.67%
98.5	38	31.67
103.5	72	60.00
108.5	100	83.33
113.5	112	93.33
118.5	118	98.33
123.5	120	100.00

The percentage cumulative frequencies are plotted against the variate on arithmetic probability paper (Fig. 5.15). The closeness to which the plotted points conform to a straight line determines whether the distribution is approximately normal or not. From Fig. 5.15 we see that the given distribution may, for all practical purposes, be accepted as normal.

The mean and standard deviation may also be found from Fig. 5.15. For a normal distribution, the mean is the value of the variate corresponding to a cumulative percentage frequency of 50%. Thus the mean for this distribution is approximately 102 kN (the correct value is 101.9 kN). Also, for a normal distribution, the area under the normal curve between the mean and 1 standard deviation is 0.3413 or 34.13% (see Table 5.1). Hence we can find an estimate of the standard deviation by finding the difference, along the horizontal axis, between the mean and a point whose ordinate is 50 − 34.13 = 15.87%. The standard deviation on Fig. 5.15 is found to be 7.4 kN approximately. (Its correct value is 7.33 kN.)

HOW ARITHMETIC PROBABILITY PAPER IS CONSTRUCTED

Plotted on ordinary linear scales the graph of percentage cumulative frequency against maximum load gives an ogive (Fig. 5.16). The problem is to convert this ogive into a straight line. To do this the distance between 50% and $P\%$ on the vertical scale must be made proportional to $u = \dfrac{x - \bar{x}}{\sigma}$.

These values of u may be found from the table of areas under the normal curve (Table 5.1).

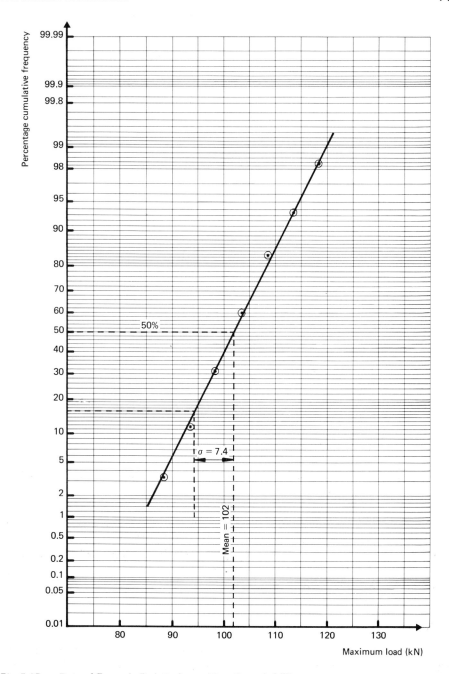

Fig. 5.15. Data of Example 5 plotted on arithmetic probability paper

For instance if $P = 70\%$, $P - 50 = 20\%$ or 0.2. The value of u corresponding to an area of 0.2 under the normal curve is 0.52. Hence on the arithmetic probability paper the distance between 50% and 70% (and 30% and 50%) is made proportional to 0.52. The table which follows gives values of u corresponding to various percentages.

% cumulative frequency	50	40 60	30 70	20 80	10 90	5 95	4 96	3 97	2 98	1 99
u		0	0.25	0.52	0.84	1.28	1.64	1.75	1.88	2.05	2.33

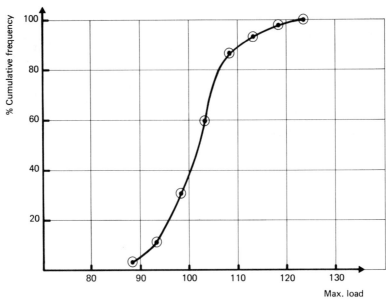

Fig. 5.16

THE NORMAL DISTRIBUTION AS AN APPROXIMATION TO THE BINOMIAL DISTRIBUTION

If n (the sample size) is large and p (the fraction defective) is not too small, the binomial distribution is closely approximated by a Normal distribution whose mean is $\bar{x} = np$ and whose standard deviation is $\sigma = \sqrt{npq}$. In practice, the approximation is very good if both np and nq are greater than 5.

EXAMPLE 5

A manufacturer knows that, on the average, 2% of the articles he produces are defective. Estimate the probability that in a sample of 1000 articles there will be 28 or more defective articles.

Here $\qquad \bar{x} = np = 1000 \times 0.02 = 20$

and $\qquad \sigma = \sqrt{npq} = \sqrt{1000 \times 0.02 \times 0.98} = 4.43$

when $\qquad x = 28, \quad u = \dfrac{x - \bar{x}}{\sigma} = \dfrac{28 - 20}{4.43} = 1.81$

The probability of the sample containing 28 or more defective articles is given by the tail area beyond $u = 1.81$. This is $0.5 - 0.464\,9 = 0.035\,1 = 3.51\%$. Hence 3.51% of all the samples of 1000 articles taken are likely to contain 28 or more defective articles.

EXERCISE 6

In the following questions $u = \dfrac{x - \bar{x}}{\sigma}$.

1) If $\bar{x} = 20$ and $\sigma = 4$, find the values of u corresponding to:
(a) $x = 16$ (b) $x = 18$ (c) $x = 21$ (d) $x = 26$

2) Using Table 5.1, find areas under the normal curve between:
(a) $u = 0$ and $u = 1.40$ (b) $u = -0.83$ and $u = 0$
(c) $u = -0.42$ and $u = 1.32$ (d) $u = -2.56$ and $u = -1.64$
(e) $u = -1.78$ and $u = -1.34$

3) Using Table 5.1, find the following tail areas under the normal curve:
(a) beyond $u = 2.41$ (b) beyond $u = 0.86$
(c) up to $u = -1.39$ (d) up to $u = -2.17$

4) By measuring a large number of items produced on an automatic lathe it was found that their mean length was 20.06 mm with a standard deviation of 0.04 mm. Find the probability that one component taken at random would have:

(a) a length less than 19.98 mm,
(b) a length greater than 20.16 mm,
(c) a length between 20.00 mm and 20.10 mm.

5) In mass producing a bush it was found that the mean outside diameter was 12.50 mm with a standard deviation of 0.015 mm. In a batch of 2000 bushes how many can be expected to have an outside diameter between 12.48 mm and 12.53 mm?

6) In a certain factory 1000 electric lamps are installed. These lamps have a mean burning life of 1100 hours with a standard deviation of 250 hours. How many lamps are likely to fail during the first 800 burning hours and how many lamps are likely to fail between 900 and 1400 burning hours?

7) As a result of testing 300 oil filled capacitors the following frequency distribution was obtained:

Capacity (μF)	19.96	19.97	19.98	19.99	20.00	20.01	20.02	20.03	20.04
Frequency	1	6	25	72	93	69	27	6	1

By using probability paper establish if the distribution is normal or not and estimate the mean and standard deviation.

8) A group of 200 castings is weighed with the following results.

Mass (kg)	168	168.5	169	169.5	170	170.5	171	171.5	172
Frequency	2	2	28	44	50	38	26	6	4

Is the distribution approximately normal? If so estimate the mean and standard deviation.

9) Components produced on a machine tool are known to be 2% defective. What is the probability that a sample of 600 components will contain 15 or more defective components.

10) In a sample of 1500 articles it is found that, on the average, 15 articles are defective. What is the probability that a sample of 1500 articles will contain between 13 and 18 defective articles.

11) By measuring 100 parts it was found that the diameter of a turned bar had a mean of 35.03 mm with a standard deviation of 0.03 mm. If the specification limits are 35.00 ± 0.08 mm determine the percentage of parts likely to be produced outside limits.

12) The table below gives the life, in hours, of radio parts. If the parts have a guaranteed life of 350 hours find the percentage likely to be produced which will not meet this specification.

Life (hours)	300–399	400–499	500–599	600–699	700–799
Frequency	7	23	29	38	34

Life (hours)	800–899	900–999	1000–1099	1100–1199
Frequency	31	24	11	3

Chapter 6

Sampling and Estimation Theory

After reaching the end of this chapter you should be able to:

1) Describe the concept of a sampling distribution.

2) Relate the mean and standard deviation of the sampling distribution to the mean and standard deviation of the parent population.

3) Recognise that the distribution for $\bar{x}$ is approximately normal when the sample size is not too small.

4) Calculate confidence interval estimates for the population mean using a sample from a population with a known standard deviation.

5) Determine unbiased estimates of the population mean and standard deviation from sample data.

6) Use the 't' distribution to calculate the confidence interval for the population mean using a sample from a population with unknown standard deviation.

SAMPLING DISTRIBUTIONS

Suppose that from a parent population we take a large number of samples each containing n items. We can calculate the mean for each of the samples and hence form a distribution for the sample means.

The samples which are chosen must be representative of the population. Representative samples may be obtained by *random sampling* in which each item of the population has an equal chance of being included in the sample. One way of obtaining a random sample is to give each item in the population a number and conduct a raffle. A second way is to use a table of *random numbers*, part of which is shown below, to obtain the sample.

RANDOM NUMBERS

50532	25496	95652	42657	73557	76152
50020	24819	52984	76168	07136	40876
79971	54195	25708	51817	36732	72484

EXAMPLE 1

The table below gives the diameters of 100 turned bars produced on an automatic lathe.

Diameter (mm)	Frequency
44.96	8
44.97	21
44.98	43
44.99	20
45.00	8

Three samples, each containing 5 items, are required from this population. Using a table of random numbers show how the samples are obtained.

Using two digits to number each of the 100 bars, the 8 bars of 44.96 mm diameter are numbered 00, 01, 02, 03, 04, 05, 06 and 07. The 21 bars of 44.97 mm diameter are numbered 08 to 28 and so on as shown in the table below.

Diameter (mm)	Frequency	Sampling number
44.96	8	00–07
44.97	21	08–28
44.98	43	29–71
44.99	20	72–91
45.00	8	92–99

Sampling numbers are now taken from the table of random numbers given above. From the first line the sequence 50, 53, 22, 54 and 96 is obtained. Hence the first sample will comprise of bars numbered 50, 53, 22, 54 and 96. Carrying on in this way we find the second sample to comprise of bars numbered 95, 65, 24, 26 and 57. The third sample comprises of bars numbered 73, 55, 77, 61 and 52.

A population may be finite or it may be infinite. If we draw 5 balls successively from a box containing 100 balls, without replacing them, we are sampling from a finite population. If, however, we replace each ball after drawing it we are sampling from an infinite population, since theoretically we may draw any number of samples without exhausting the population.

In practice, sampling without replacement from a very large population may be considered as sampling from an infinite population.

DISTRIBUTION OF SAMPLE MEANS

If the population consists of n_p items it can be shown that:

$$\bar{x} = \mu$$

and
$$s_{\bar{x}} = \frac{\sigma}{\sqrt{n}} \sqrt{\frac{n_p - n}{n_p - 1}}$$

where μ = the mean of the population

$\bar{x}$ = the mean of the sampling distribution

σ = the standard deviation of the population

$s_{\bar{x}}$ = the standard deviation of the sampling distribution

and n = the number of items in each sample

If the population is infinite, or the sampling is with replacement then the results given above reduce to:

$$\bar{x} = \mu \quad \text{and} \quad s_{\bar{x}} = \frac{\sigma}{\sqrt{n}}$$

For values of n equal to, or greater than 30, the distribution for the sample means is approximately a normal distribution with a mean of $\bar{x}$ and standard deviation of $s_{\bar{x}}$ irrespective of whether the population itself is a normal distribution. The approximation to the normal distribution gets better as n gets larger.

If the population is normally distributed and σ is known the distribution for sample means is normally distributed even for small values of n (Fig. 6.1).

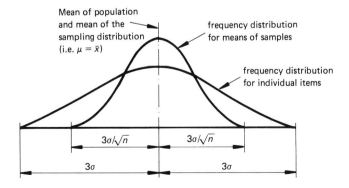

Fig. 6.1. The frequency curve for the sample means is a normal curve whose standard deviation is $\sigma/\sqrt{n}$

STANDARD ERROR OF THE DISTRIBUTION OF SAMPLE MEANS

The standard deviation of a sampling distribution statistic is called the *standard error*. Thus for the distribution of sample means the standard error is $s_{\bar{x}} = \dfrac{\sigma}{\sqrt{n}}$.

EXAMPLE 2

A population consists of the five numbers 1, 2, 3, 4 and 5. Find:

(a) the mean and standard deviation of the population,
(b) the mean and standard deviation of all the possible samples of size 2 which can be drawn with replacement from this population.

(a) The mean of the population is:

$$\mu = \frac{1 + 2 + 3 + 4 + 5}{5} = \frac{15}{5} = 3$$

The standard deviation of the population is:

$$\sigma = \sqrt{\frac{\sum x^2}{N} - \mu^2}$$

$$= \sqrt{\frac{1^2 + 2^2 + 3^2 + 4^2 + 5^2}{5} - 3^2}$$

$$= \sqrt{2} = 1.414$$

(b) There are 25 samples of size 2 which can be drawn, with replacement, from the population. They are:

$$
\begin{array}{lllll}
1,1 & 2,1 & 3,1 & 4,1 & 5,1 \\
1,2 & 2,2 & 3,2 & 4,2 & 5,2 \\
1,3 & 2,3 & 3,3 & 4,3 & 5,3 \\
1,4 & 2,4 & 3,4 & 4,4 & 5,4 \\
1,5 & 2,5 & 3,5 & 4,5 & 5,5 \\
\end{array}
$$

The corresponding sample means are:

$$
\begin{array}{lllll}
1.0 & 1.5 & 2.0 & 2.5 & 3.0 \\
1.5 & 2.0 & 2.5 & 3.0 & 3.5 \\
2.0 & 2.5 & 3.0 & 3.5 & 4.0 \\
2.5 & 3.0 & 3.5 & 4.0 & 4.5 \\
3.0 & 3.5 & 4.0 & 4.5 & 5.0 \\
\end{array}
$$

The mean of the sampling distribution is:

$$\bar{x} = \frac{\text{sum of all the sample means}}{\text{number of samples}} = \frac{75}{25} = 3$$

This illustrates the fact that:

$$\bar{x} = \mu$$

The standard deviation of the sampling distribution is:

$$s_{\bar{x}} = \sqrt{\frac{\sum \bar{x}_i^2}{N} - \bar{x}^2}$$

where $\bar{x}_i$ = the means of the ith sample

and N = the number of samples taken

$$s_{\bar{x}} = \sqrt{\frac{250}{25} - 3^2} = 1$$

This illustrates the fact that for sampling with replacement:

$$s_{\bar{x}} = \frac{\sigma}{\sqrt{n}} = \frac{\sqrt{2}}{\sqrt{2}} = 1$$

EXAMPLE 3

The heights of 2000 male factory workers are normally distributed with a mean of 172 cm and a standard deviation of 7.5 cm. If 40 samples each containing 30 workers are taken, determine the mean and standard deviation of the sampling distribution for sample means if:

(a) the sampling is done with replacement.
(b) the sampling is done without replacement.

(a) $\bar{x} = \mu = 172$ cm

$$s_{\bar{x}} = \frac{\sigma}{\sqrt{n}} = \frac{7.5}{\sqrt{30}} = 1.369 \text{ cm}$$

(b) $\bar{x} = \mu = 172$ cm

$$s_{\bar{x}} = \frac{\sigma}{\sqrt{n}} \sqrt{\frac{n_p - n}{n_p - 1}} = \frac{7.5}{\sqrt{30}} \sqrt{\frac{2000 - 30}{2000 - 1}} = 1.359 \text{ cm}$$

Thus the value of $s_{\bar{x}}$ for sampling done without replacement is only slightly less than that for sampling done with replacement. Hence the population of 2000 is large enough to be considered an infinite population.

EXAMPLE 4

A very large batch of ball bearings has a mean diameter of 25.02 mm with a standard deviation of 0.30 mm. A random sample of 100 of these ball bearings is taken. Find:

(a) the probability that the mean of the sample lies between 24.96 mm and 25.00 mm,
(b) the probability that the mean of the sample is greater than 25.10 mm.

For the sampling distribution of means

$$\bar{x} = \mu = 25.02 \text{ mm}$$

$$s_{\bar{x}} = \frac{\sigma}{\sqrt{n}} = \frac{0.30}{\sqrt{100}} = 0.03 \text{ mm}$$

(a) When $\bar{x} = 24.96$ mm, $u_1 = \frac{\bar{x} - \mu}{s_{\bar{x}}} = \frac{24.96 - 25.02}{0.03} = -2.00.$

When $\bar{x} = 25.00$ mm, $u_2 = \frac{\bar{x} - \mu}{s_{\bar{x}}} = \frac{25.00 - 25.02}{0.03} = -0.67.$

Since $n > 30$ we may use the normal distribution to determine probabilities. From Table 5.1 and Fig. 6.2,

area between $u = -2.00$ and $u = 0 = 0.477\,2$

area between $u = -0.67$ and $u = 0 = 0.248\,6$

area between $u = -2.0$ and $u = -0.67 = 0.477\,2 - 0.248\,6$
$$= 0.228\,6$$

Hence the probability that the mean of the sample lies between 24.96 mm and 25.00 mm is 0.228 6.

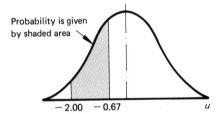

Probability is given by shaded area

−2.00 −0.67 u

Fig. 6.2

(b) When $\bar{x} = 25.10$, $u = \frac{25.10 - 25.02}{0.03} = 2.67.$

From Table 5.1 and Fig. 6.3,

area between $u = 0$ and $u = 2.67 = 0.496\,2$

tail area beyond $u = 2.67 = 0.5 - 0.496\,2 = 0.003\,8$

Hence the probability that the mean of the sample is greater than 25.10 mm is 0.003 8.

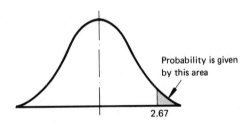

Probability is given by this area

2.67

Fig. 6.3

CONFIDENCE LIMITS

It is seldom possible to measure every item in a population to find the mean of that population. Hence we must resort to sampling. To estimate the mean of a population we take a sample from the population and calculate the mean of the sample. As we have previously seen, we then regard the mean of the sample as an estimate of the mean of the population. This estimate is called a *point estimate* of the mean of the population because it is a single number.

To determine the reliability of the point estimate of the population mean we use confidence limits. We know, from Table 5.1, that for a normal distribution of sample means only 5% of these sample means are likely to lie outside the limits of $\mu \pm \dfrac{1.96\sigma}{\sqrt{n}}$ (see Fig. 6.4). We say that at the 95% confidence level the true mean of the population is unlikely to lie outside the limits of $\bar{x} \pm \dfrac{1.96\sigma}{\sqrt{n}}$, $\bar{x}$ being the mean of the sample.

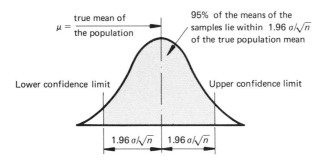

Fig. 6.4.   The 95% confidence level

The most commonly used confidence levels are the 95%, 99% and 99.9% levels. The table below shows the limits for these confidence levels.

Confidence level	95%	99%	99.9%
Limits	$\bar{x} \pm \dfrac{1.96\sigma}{\sqrt{n}}$	$\bar{x} \pm \dfrac{2.58\sigma}{\sqrt{n}}$	$\bar{x} \pm \dfrac{3.29\sigma}{\sqrt{n}}$

These confidence limits are examples of *interval estimates* of the population mean because we are stating limits between which the population mean may be expected to lie. Although the sample mean is useful as an estimate of the population mean there is no way by which we can express the accuracy of the estimate. (In fact, mathematically speaking, the probability of the mean of the sample exactly equalling the mean of the population is $p = 0$.) However, by using confidence limits, the degree of accuracy of the estimate is given by the confidence level.

EXAMPLE 5

The diameters of a random sample of 100 turned bars were measured and their mean diameter was found to be 18.10 mm. The standard deviation for the population is known to be 1.2 mm. At the 99% confidence level, what is the estimate of the mean diameter of all the turned bars produced?

From the table above, the limits for the 99% confidence level are

$$\bar{x} \pm \frac{2.58\sigma}{\sqrt{n}} = 18.10 \pm \frac{2.58 \times 1.2}{\sqrt{100}} = 18.10 \pm 0.31 \text{ mm}$$

We can be 99% certain that the true mean of the population lies between 17.79 mm and 18.41 mm.

UNBIASED ESTIMATES OF POPULATION MEAN AND STANDARD DEVIATION

An *unbiased estimator* is a sample statistic (such as the mean of a sample) whose expected value is equal to the population parameter (for example, the population mean). The mean of a sampling distribution for sample means is an unbiased estimate for the mean of the population because its value is expected to be equal to the population mean.

The unbiased estimate for the standard deviation of a population is:

$$\hat{s} = s\sqrt{\frac{n-1}{n}}$$

where $\hat{s}$ = the unbiased estimate of the population standard deviation (i.e. $\hat{s} = \sigma$).

   s = standard deviation of the sample

   n = the sample size

EXAMPLE 6

A sample of 5 resistors were checked with the following results: 12.6, 12.7, 12.5, 12.6 and 12.8 ohm. Determine the unbiased estimates of the mean and standard deviation of the population from which the resistors were drawn.

$$\bar{x} = \frac{12.6 + 12.7 + 12.5 + 12.6 + 12.8}{5} = \frac{63.2}{5} = 12.64 \text{ ohm}$$

This is an unbiased estimate of the population mean.

$$s = \sqrt{\frac{\sum x^2}{n} - \bar{x}^2} = \sqrt{\frac{798.9}{5} - 12.64^2}$$

$$= \sqrt{0.0104} \quad = 0.102 \text{ mm}$$

This is an estimate of the standard deviation of the population but it is not unbiased.

The unbiased estimate of the population standard deviation is

$$\hat{s} = \sqrt{\frac{n-1}{n}}\, s = 0.102 \times \sqrt{\frac{5-1}{5}} = 0.081\,6 \text{ ohm}$$

(Note that for large samples $(n \geqslant 30)$ the correction $\sqrt{\dfrac{n-1}{n}}$ is insignificant. Hence for large samples the unbiased estimate of σ may be taken to be s.)

THE t-DISTRIBUTION

On page 77 it was stated that the normal distribution may be used to estimate a population mean for any large sample $(n \geqslant 30)$ and for a small sample $(n < 30)$ only if the population is normally distributed and σ is known.

In this section we consider the situation in which the sample is small and the population is normally distributed but σ is not known.

Let us define t by the equation:

$$t = \frac{\bar{x} - \mu}{\hat{s}/\sqrt{n}}$$

which is analogous to:

$$u = \frac{\bar{x} - \mu}{s_{\bar{x}}} = \frac{\bar{x} - \mu}{\sigma/\sqrt{n}} \quad \text{(see page 80)}$$

Now

$$\hat{s} = s\sqrt{\frac{n}{n-1}}$$

$\therefore$

$$t = \frac{|\bar{x} - \mu|\sqrt{n-1}}{s}$$

This latter formula for t includes s in the denominator. Now s, the standard deviation of the sample, is not a constant as is σ, but varies with each sample mean. The result is that the values of t are not distributed in the same way as the values of u.

From a normal distribution (i.e. a population with a normal distribution curve) whose standard deviation is not known, let us take a number of samples of size n. For each sample let us calculate the value of t using the mean of the sample, $\bar{x}$, and the standard deviation of the sample, s, as shown in Example 7.

EXAMPLE 7

A sample of 5 items is taken from a population which is normally distributed. If the mean of the population is 17.2 mm and the mean and standard deviation are 18.0 mm and 0.5 mm respectively, calculate the value of t.

$$\hat{s} = s\sqrt{\frac{n}{n-1}} = 0.5 \times \sqrt{\frac{5}{5-1}} = 0.56 \text{ mm}$$

$$t = \frac{|\bar{x} - \mu|}{\hat{s}/\sqrt{n}} = \frac{|18.0 - 17.2|}{0.56/\sqrt{5}} = \frac{0.8 \times \sqrt{5}}{0.56} = 3.19$$

From these calculated values of t a distribution curve is obtained and the distribution is called a *t-distribution*. By varying the sample size a series of distribution curves similar to those shown in Fig. 6.5 are obtained. The curves show that when the sample is large $(n \geqslant 30)$ the t-distribution is very nearly normal. However, when the samples are small the t-distribution is no longer normal and its approximation to the normal distribution gets worse as the sample size decreases.

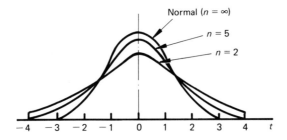

Fig. 6.5

This means that when the sample is large $(n \geqslant 30)$ we may use the normal distribution to determine confidence limits (see page 81). However, when the sample is small $(n < 30)$ the t-distribution must be used to determine the confidence limits.

Table 6.1 shows the t-distribution in which values of t are tabulated against degrees of freedom. The number of degrees of freedom for a single sample is:

$$\text{d.f.} = n - 1$$

that is, the number of degrees of freedom is one less than the number of items in the sample.

CONFIDENCE LIMITS FOR SMALL SAMPLES

As was done with the normal distribution we can define the 95% and the 99% confidence limits by using the table of the t-distribution (Table 6.1).

Table 6.1   The 't' distribution

Significance level	5%		1%	
	One-tailed test	Two-tailed test	One-tailed test	Two-tailed test
1	6.314	12.706	31.821	63.657
2	2.920	4.303	6.965	9.925
3	2.353	3.182	4.541	5.841
4	2.132	2.776	3.747	4.604
5	2.015	2.571	3.365	4.032
6	1.943	2.447	3.143	3.707
7	1.895	2.365	2.998	3.499
8	1.860	2.306	2.896	3.355
9	1.833	2.262	2.821	3.250
10	1.812	2.228	2.764	3.169
11	1.796	2.201	2.718	3.106
12	1.782	2.179	2.681	3.055
13	1.771	2.160	2.650	3.012
14	1.761	2.145	2.624	2.977
15	1.753	2.131	2.602	2.947
16	1.746	2.120	2.583	2.921
17	1.740	2.110	2.567	2.898
18	1.734	2.101	2.552	2.878
19	1.729	2.093	2.539	2.861
20	1.725	2.086	2.528	2.845
21	1.721	2.080	2.518	2.831
22	1.717	2.074	2.508	2.819
23	1.714	2.069	2.500	2.807
24	1.711	2.064	2.492	2.797
25	1.708	2.060	2.485	2.787
26	1.706	2.056	2.479	2.779
27	1.703	2.052	2.473	2.771
28	1.701	2.048	2.467	2.763
29	1.699	2.045	2.462	2.756
30	1.697	2.042	2.457	2.750

We can represent the confidence limits for a population mean by:

$$\bar{x} \pm t_c \frac{\sigma}{\sqrt{n}}$$

where t_c is the value of t obtained from Table 6.1.

Fig. 6.6 shows how the 95% confidence limits are obtained.

Since both tails of the t-distribution curve are used we look up the value of t_c in the 'two-tailed test' column.

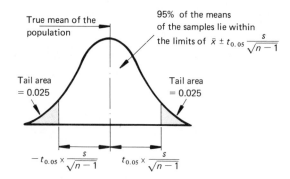

Fig. 6.6

Since σ, the standard deviation of the population is generally unknown we use the unbiased estimate for σ which is:

$$\hat{s} = s\sqrt{\frac{n}{n-1}}$$

Hence the confidence limits for a population mean is given by:

$$\bar{x} \pm t_c \times \sqrt{\frac{n}{n-1}} \times s \times \frac{1}{\sqrt{n}} = \bar{x} \pm \frac{t_c s}{\sqrt{n-1}}$$

where $\bar{x} =$ the mean of the sample

$t_c =$ the value of t for a two-tailed test

$s =$ standard deviation of the sample

$n =$ number of items in the sample

EXAMPLE 8

The diameters of a random sample of 10 ball bearings were measured and their mean diameter was found to be 4.38 mm with a standard deviation of 0.06 mm. Find:

(a) the 95%,
(b) the 99% confidence limits for the population mean from which the sample was taken.

(a) The 95% confidence limits are given by:

$$\bar{x} \pm t_{0.05} \times \frac{s}{\sqrt{n-1}}$$

Since d.f. $= 10 - 1 = 9$, $t_{0.05} = 2.262$.

Also $\bar{x} = 4.38\,\text{mm}$, $s = 0.06\,\text{mm}$ and $n = 10$.

$$\therefore \qquad \bar{x} \pm t_{0.05} \times \frac{s}{\sqrt{n-1}} = 4.38 \pm 2.262 \times \frac{0.06}{\sqrt{9}}$$

$$= 4.38 \pm 0.045$$

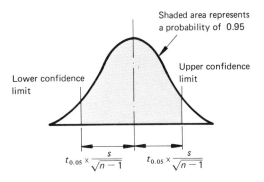

Fig. 6.7

Hence we can be 95% certain that the mean of the population of ball bearings lies between 4.335 mm and 4.425 mm (see Fig. 6.7).

(b) The 99% confidence limits are given by

$$\bar{x} \pm t_{0.01} \times \frac{s}{\sqrt{n-1}}$$

For d.f. $= 9$, $t_{0.01} = 3.250$

$$\therefore \quad \bar{x} \pm t_{0.01} \times \frac{s}{\sqrt{n-1}} = 4.38 \pm 3.250 \times \frac{0.06}{\sqrt{9}}$$

$$= 4.38 \pm 0.065$$

We can be 99% certain that the mean of the population of ball bearings lies between 4.315 mm and 4.445 mm. (Note that in obtaining the confidence limits a 'two-tailed' value for t is used.)

EXERCISE 7

1) The diameters of 5000 electric motor shafts are normally distributed with a mean of 50.42 mm and a standard deviation of 1.23 mm. If 80 samples each containing 30 shafts are obtained find the expected mean and standard deviation of the sampling distribution for sample means if the sampling was done:

(a) With replacement.
(b) Without replacement.
(c) How many samples are likely to have a mean between 50.32 mm and 50.48 mm?

2) 400 resistors have a mean resistance of 50.2 ohm and a standard deviation of 0.5 ohm. Find the probability that a random sample of 50 of these resistors would have a resistance:

(a) between 50.2 ohm and 50.3 ohm,
(b) less than 50.05 ohm,
(c) greater than 50.18 ohm.

3) A population consists of the four numbers 2, 6, 10 and 14. Consider all the samples of size two which can be drawn, with replacement, from this population. Calculate:

(a) the population mean,
(b) the population standard deviation,
(c) the mean of the sampling distribution for means,
(d) the standard deviation of the sampling distribution for means.
(e) Verify (c) and (d) by using suitable formulae.

4) The masses of 3000 ball bearings are normally distributed with a mean of 635 grams and a standard deviation of 1.4 grams. If 70 samples each containing 36 ball bearings are taken from this population, find the expected mean and standard deviation of the distribution of samples if the sampling is done:

(a) with replacement,
(b) without replacement.

5) A sample of 5 components produced on a machine tool were measured. Their lengths were found to be 18.99, 19.11, 19.08, 18.96 and 19.10 mm. Determine the unbiased estimates of:

(a) the mean of the large batch from which this sample was drawn,
(b) the standard deviation of the batch.

6) The heights of 100 male factory workers represent a random sample of the heights of all 1972 male workers in the factory. The mean height of the 100 men measured was 1.727 m with a standard deviation of 0.05 m. Determine unbiased estimates of:

(a) the mean height of the population,
(b) the standard deviation of the population.

7) A random sample is drawn from a population with a known standard deviation of 2.0.

(a) Calculate the standard error of the sample mean if the sample size is:
     (i) 9   (ii) 25   (iii) 100
(b) If the sample mean is 25.3, calculate the 95% confidence limits if the sample size is:
     (i) 9   (ii) 25   (iii) 100

8) The percentage of zinc in a certain alloy is measured six times. The standard deviation of these measurements is 2.5% and the mean of the six measurements is 14.1%. Determine the 95% confidence limits for the true percentage of zinc assuming:

(a) that the measurements are normally distributed,
(b) that the 't' distribution is applicable.

9) The diameter of a sphere is measured 10 times. The mean of these

measurements is found to be 53.6 mm with a standard deviation of 0.8 mm. Find:

(a) 95%,
(b) 99% confidence limits for the true diameter of the sphere using the 't' distribution.

10) If in question 9, the measurements were normally distributed, determine

(a) 95%,
(b) 99% confidence limits

for the true diameter of the sphere.

Chapter 7 **Tests of Significance**

After reaching the end of this chapter you should be able to:

1) Explain the meaning of null hypothesis and alternative hypothesis.

2) Explain the difference between Type I and Type II errors.

3) Choose the appropriate critical region.

4) Perform a significance test for a population mean using sample data from a population with a known standard deviation.

5) Perform a significance test for a population mean using sample data from a population with an unknown standard deviation.

6) Recognise a situation in which a paired sample test is appropriate.

7) Test for a difference between two means using paired samples.

STATISTICAL DECISIONS

In Statistics we are often called upon to make decisions about populations on the basis of information obtained by taking a sample from the population.

For instance, using sample data, we may wish to decide if one type of protective coating is better than another, if a machine tool has been set high or not, etc.

HYPOTHESES

In trying to reach a decision assumptions are made about the populations involved. These assumptions are called *hypotheses*.

Frequently a hypothesis is formulated for the sole purpose of rejecting or *nullifying* it. For instance if we want to decide if one process is better than another we formulate the hypothesis that there is no difference between the processes, i.e. that any observed differences are simply due to fluctuations in samples taken from the *same* population. Such hypotheses are called *null hypotheses* and they are usually denoted by H_0.

A hypothesis which differs from the null hypothesis is called the *alternative hypothesis* and it is denoted by H_1. Thus in the above example the alternative hypothesis might be that the second process is better than the first.

EXAMPLE 1

An accountant wishes to test the assumption that the mean value of all invoices sent out by a firm is £2600. He takes a sample of 36 invoices and calculates the mean of this sample. He wishes to reject the assumed mean of £2600 only if it is cleary contradicted by the sample mean. Formulate the null and alternative hypotheses.

The null hypothesis is

$$H_0: \mu = £2600 \quad \text{(the mean equals £2600)}$$

The alternative hypothesis is

$$H_1: \mu \neq £2600 \quad \text{(the mean does not equal £2600)}$$

SIGNIFICANCE TESTS

These are tests which enable us to reject or accept the null hypothesis.

TYPE I AND TYPE II ERRORS

A Type I error is made when a null hypothesis is rejected when it should have been accepted.

A Type II error is made when a null hypothesis is accepted when it should have been rejected (see Example 5).

LEVEL OF SIGNIFICANCE

The maximum probability with which we risk making a Type I error is called the *level of significance* of the test. When a 5% level of significance is specified there is a probability of 0.05 of rejecting the null hypothesis when it is true. Similarly when a significance level of 1% is used there is a probability of 0.01 that the null hypothesis will be rejected when it is true.

SIGNIFICANCE TEST USING THE NORMAL DISTRIBUTION

We often wish to compare means to see if the difference between them is due to chance only or if there are real reasons for the difference.

The normal distribution may be used for testing the null hypothesis for a population mean if the sample size is greater or equal to 30 $(n \geqslant 30)$ or when $n < 30$ if the population is normally distributed and its standard deviation is known.

The relationship

$$u = \frac{\bar{x} - \mu}{\sigma/\sqrt{n}}$$

is used when we want to test the assumption that a sample of size n whose mean is $\bar{x}$ could have been drawn from a population whose mean is μ and whose standard deviation is σ.

EXAMPLE 2

A manufacturer of light bulbs states that the mean life of his bulbs is 1600 hours with a standard deviation of 120 hours. A sample of 64 such bulbs was checked and the mean life of the bulbs was found to be 1560 hours. At the 1% level of significance can we reject the manufacturer's claim?

We take the null hypothesis to be:

$$H_0\!: \mu = 1600 \text{ hours} \quad \text{(the mean life is } 1600 \text{ hours)}$$

The alternative hypothesis is

$$H_1\!: \mu < 1600 \text{ hours} \quad \text{(the mean life is less than } 1600 \text{ hours)}$$

We are given $\mu = 1600$, $\bar{x} = 1560$, $\sigma = 120$ and $n = 64$.

$$u = \frac{\bar{x} - \mu}{\sigma/\sqrt{n}} = \frac{1560 - 1600}{120/\sqrt{64}}$$

$$= \frac{-40 \times 8}{120} = -2.67$$

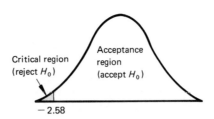

Critical region
(reject H_0)

Acceptance region
(accept H_0)

-2.58

Fig. 7.1

Fig. 7.1 shows the regions under the normal distribution curve for which we can accept or reject the null hypothesis. For a 1% level of significance the area of the critical region is 0.01. From Table 5.1 we find that for a tail area of 0.01 the value of u is 2.58. This is called the *critical value* for the 1% level of significance. Since the calculated value of u is -2.67 we are in the critical region and hence we reject H_0. We can be 99% certain that the burning life of the bulbs is less than 1600 hours. We therefore reject the manufacturer's claim.

ONE AND TWO-TAILED TESTS

In Example 2 we used only one tail of the probability curve because we wished to decide if μ was less than 1600 hours. When a one-tailed test is used the area of the critical region is equal to the level of significance.

Suppose in Example 2 we wished to formulate:

$$H_0: \mu = 1600 \text{ hours} \quad \text{(the mean is 1600 hours)}$$

$$H_1: \mu \neq 1600 \text{ hours} \quad \text{(the mean is not 1600 hours)}$$

In this case we are interested in the probabilities of μ being greater than 1600 hours and also in μ being less than 1600 hours. In such cases a two-tailed test is used (Fig. 7.2) and the *sum* of the two tail areas, representing the critical regions, is equal to the level of significance.

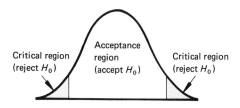

Critical region (reject H_0)   Acceptance region (accept H_0)   Critical region (reject H_0)

Fig. 7.2

CRITICAL VALUES

From the table of areas under the normal curve (Table 5.1) we find the critical values of u corresponding to various levels of significance to be as shown in Table 7.1. Critical values for other levels of significance may be obtained from Table 5.1.

Table 7.1   Critical values of u

Level of significance	5%	1%	0.1%
Critical value of u for one-tailed tests	+ 1.65 or − 1.65	+ 2.33 or − 2.33	+ 3.09 or − 3.09
Critical value of u for two-tailed tests	± 1.96	± 2.58	± 3.29

EXAMPLE 3

In the past a machine has produced ball bearings with a mean diameter of 15.00 mm and a standard deviation of 0.60 mm. To determine whether the process is in control a sample of 50 bearings was checked and their mean was found to be 15.20 mm. Is the process in control?

The null and alternative hypotheses are taken as:

$H_0: \mu = 15.00$ mm   (the population mean has remained at 15.00 mm and the process is in control)

$H_1: \mu \neq 15.00$ mm   (the population mean has altered from 15.00 mm and the process is not in control)

We have $\mu = 15.00$, $\bar{x} = 15.20$, $\sigma = 0.60$ and $n = 50$.

$$u = \frac{15.20 - 15.00}{0.60/\sqrt{50}} = \frac{0.20 \times \sqrt{50}}{0.60} = 2.36$$

A two-tailed test is used because we are checking to see if μ is less than 15.00 mm or more than 15.00 mm. From Table 7.1 we see that at the 5% significance level the critical values of u are ± 1.96. Hence at the 5% significant level we reject H_0. We can be 95% certain that all is not well with the process. In practice a second sample would be checked immediately.

STANDARD DEVIATION OF THE POPULATION NOT KNOWN

Frequently the standard deviation of the population is not known and it has to be estimated from the standard deviation of the sample. If the sample size is greater or equal to 30 $(n \geqslant 30)$ it may be assumed that s, the sample standard deviation, is equal to σ, the population standard deviation.

EXAMPLE 4

The breaking strengths of cables made by a certain firm are stated to have a mean strength of 7500 N. A sample of 64 of these cables is checked and the mean strength is found to be 7400 N with a standard deviation of 400 N. Can the statement that the mean strength is 7500 N be supported at the 5% level of significance?

We formulate the hypotheses:

$H_0: \mu = 7500$ N   (the mean strength is 7500 N)

$H_1: \mu < 7500$ N   (the mean strength is less than 7500 N)

Since $n \geqslant 30$ we take $\sigma = s = 400$ N.

$$u = \frac{\bar{x} - \mu}{\sigma/\sqrt{n}} = \frac{7400 - 7500}{400/\sqrt{64}}$$

$$= \frac{-100 \times 8}{400} = -2.00$$

A one-tailed test is appropriate and at the 5% significance level the critical value of u is $u_{CR} = -1.65$. Hence we are 95% certain that the mean strength of the cables is less than 7500 N (see Fig. 7.3).

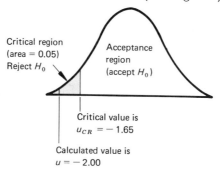

Fig. 7.3

EXAMPLE 5

A firm manufacturing a certain type of chain finds that its mean breaking strength is 6.00 kN with a standard deviation of 0.48 kN. A new process is developed which, it is thought, will increase the breaking strength of the chains. To test if this is so a sample of 64 chains produced by the new process is taken.

(a) Find the critical value for the mean of the sample, at the 1% significance level, which will allow the null hypothesis, $H_0: \mu = 6.00$ kN to be rejected, and the alternative hypothesis, $H_1: \mu > 6.00$ kN, to be accepted.

(b) Calculate the probability of accepting H_0 when the mean breaking strength is actually 6.20 kN, assuming the standard deviation remains at 0.48 kN.

(a) For a one-tailed test at the 1% level of significance, the critical value of u from Table 7.1 is:

$$u_{CR} = 2.33$$

Hence we reject H_0 if the calculated value of u is greater than 2.33 (i.e. $u > 2.33$). Since:

$$u = \frac{\bar{x} - \mu}{\sigma/\sqrt{n}} = \frac{\bar{x} - 6.00}{0.48/\sqrt{64}} = \frac{\bar{x} - 6.00}{0.06}$$

$$\bar{x} = 0.06u + 6.00$$

The critical value of $\bar{x}$ at the 1% significance level is:

$$\bar{x} = 0.06u_{CR} + 6.00 = (0.06 \times 2.33) + 6.00 = 6.14 \text{ kN}$$

Hence we reject H_0 if $\bar{x} > 6.14$ kN and accept H_1.

Note that the probability of rejecting H_0 when μ actually equals 6.00 kN is 0.01, the level of significance used in finding the critical value of $\bar{x}$. That is, the probability of rejecting H_0 when it should have been accepted is 0.01 (see Fig. 7.4). Hence the probability of making a Type I error is 0.01.

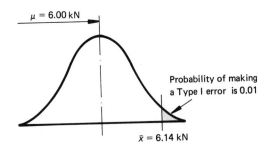

Fig. 7.4

(b) The probability of accepting H_0 when μ is actually 6.20 kN is found by first calculating:

$$u = \frac{6.14 - 6.20}{0.06} = -1.00$$

and then finding the tail area under the normal curve corresponding to $u = -1.00$. This is found to be 0.158 7 from Table 5.1.

Hence the probability of accepting H_0 when it should have been rejected is 0.158 7. That is, the probability of making a Type II error is 0.158 7 (see Fig. 7.5).

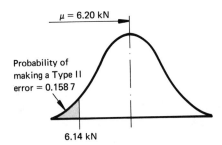

Fig. 7.5

THE OPERATING CHARACTERISTIC CURVE

The probability of making a Type II error under various hypotheses is best shown by drawing an operating characteristic curve (often abbreviated to O.C. curve).

EXAMPLE 6

Draw an O.C. curve for the chains in Example 5, assuming that the standard deviation remains at 0.48 kN.

Taking values of μ arbitrarily as 5.80, 5.90, ..., 6.3 kN and 6.4 kN, we calculate the probability of accepting $H_0: \mu = 6.00\,\text{kN}$ when we should have rejected H_0. Thus when $\mu = 6.10\,\text{kN}$,

$$u = \frac{6.14 - 6.10}{0.06} = \frac{0.04}{0.06} = 0.67$$

The area, under the normal curve, to the left of $u = 0.67$ is $0.748\,6$ (see Fig. 7.6).

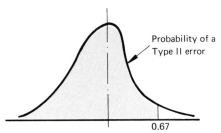

Fig. 7.6

By similar calculations the table below may be compiled.

μ	5.80	5.90	6.00	6.10	6.20	6.30	6.40
u	5.67	4.00	2.33	0.67	-1.00	-2.67	-4.33
Probability of Type II error	$1.000\,0$	$1.000\,0$	$0.990\,0$	$0.748\,6$	$0.158\,7$	$0.003\,8$	$0.000\,0$

The operating characteristic curve is shown in Fig. 7.7 where it can be seen that as the sample mean becomes progressively greater, the probability of making a Type II error progressively decreases.

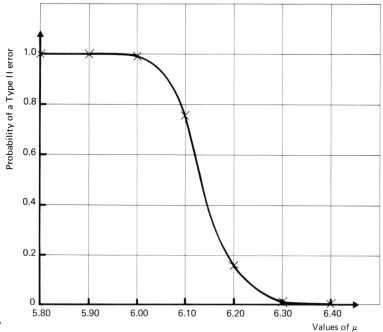

Fig. 7.7

SMALL SAMPLE THEORY

It has been previously stated that the normal distribution may be used for small samples $(n < 30)$ only if the population is normally distributed and the value of σ, the standard deviation of the population, is known.

When a population is normally distributed, the distribution for the sample means will also be normally distributed; this is true whether σ is known or not.

However if σ is unknown it has to be estimated from the values of s, the sample standard deviation. Thus as shown on page 82, for small samples $(n < 30)$,

$$\sigma = \hat{s} = \sqrt{\frac{n}{n-1}} \times s$$

Now each sample that is taken from the population will almost certainly have a standard deviation which is somewhat different to that for the other samples taken from the population. The values of the standardised variable $\dfrac{\bar{x} - \mu}{\sigma/\sqrt{n}}$ are no longer normally distributed but are distributed according to the t-distribution.

In order to compare means we first calculate:

$$t = \frac{|\bar{x} - \mu|}{\sigma/\sqrt{n}} = \frac{\sqrt{n}\,|\bar{x} - \mu|}{\sigma}$$

$$= \frac{\sqrt{n}\,|\bar{x} - \mu|}{\sqrt{\dfrac{n}{n-1}} \times s} = \frac{\sqrt{n-1}\,|\bar{x} - \mu|}{s}$$

where n is the sample size, $\bar{x}$ is the mean of the sample, μ is the mean of the population and s is the standard deviation of the sample. The symbols $|\bar{x} - \mu|$ mean that we take the value of $\bar{x} - \mu$ as positive irrespective of the values of $\bar{x}$ and μ.

EXAMPLE 7

A random sample of 10 packets of chemical had a mean mass of 15.90 kg with a standard deviation of 0.10 kg. Could this sample have been taken from a batch of packets with a mean mass of 16.00 kg?

The null and alternative hypotheses are taken as:

$H_0: \mu = 16.00$ kg   (the mean mass of the batch of packets is 16.00 kg)

$H_1: \mu \neq 16.00$ kg (the mean mass of the batch of packets is not 16.00 kg)

We have $\mu = 16.00$, $\bar{x} = 15.90$, $s = 0.10$ and $n = 10$.

$$t = \frac{\sqrt{n-1}\,|\bar{x}-\mu|}{s} = \frac{3 \times |15.90 - 16.00|}{0.10} = 3.00$$

For 9 degrees of freedom, the critical value of t for a 5% level of significance (two-tailed test) is 2.26. Hence we reject H_0 at the 5% level of
significance. We can be 95% certain that the mean mass of the batch of
the packets is not 16.00 kg.

TESTS FOR DIFFERENCE BETWEEN TWO MEANS

A problem which often occurs is that of comparing the means of two
samples. The significance tests proposed depend upon the following
assumptions:

(a) That the populations from which the samples are drawn are normally
    distributed.

(b) That the populations have the same standard deviation.

(c) That the two samples are collected independently of each other.

If the standard deviation is *known* and the normal distribution applies
then:

$$u = \frac{|\bar{x}_1 - \bar{x}_2|}{\sigma \sqrt{\dfrac{1}{n_1} + \dfrac{1}{n_2}}}$$

where $\bar{x}_1$ = the mean of the first sample

$\bar{x}_2$ = the mean of the second sample

σ = the standard deviation of the population

n_1 = the number in the first sample

n_2 = the number in the second sample

EXAMPLE 8

A component is being produced in large quantities on a machine tool. At
the start of production a sample of 50 components was checked and
their mean length was found to be 87.69 mm. Some time later a second
sample consisting of 80 components was checked and the mean length
was found to be 87.80 mm. If the standard deviation of the lengths of
the components remains unaltered at 0.85 mm, test if there is any significant difference between the means.

The null and alternative hypotheses are taken as:

$H_0: \mu_1 = \mu_2$ (the means of the populations from which
the samples were drawn are the same)

$H_1: \mu_1 \neq \mu_2$

We have, $\bar{x}_1 = 87.69$, $\bar{x}_2 = 87.80$, $\sigma = 0.85$, $n_1 = 50$ and $n_2 = 80$. Hence:

$$u = \frac{|\bar{x}_1 - \bar{x}_2|}{\sigma \sqrt{\dfrac{1}{n_1} + \dfrac{1}{n_2}}} = \frac{|87.69 - 87.80|}{0.85 \sqrt{\dfrac{1}{50} + \dfrac{1}{80}}}$$

$$= \frac{0.11}{0.153} = 0.72$$

From Table 7.1, the critical values at the 5% level for a two-tailed test are ± 1.96. Hence at the 5% level of significance we accept H_0. That is, we can say that the mean length of the components produced by the machine has not altered significantly.

If the standard deviation of the population is *not known* then the standard deviation for the difference between means is:

$$\sigma_d = \sqrt{\frac{n_1 s_1{}^2 + n_2 s_2{}^2}{n_1 + n_2 - 2}}$$

where s_1 = standard deviation of the first sample

and s_2 = standard deviation of the second sample

EXAMPLE 9

A bolt is being cold headed on two different machines. A sample is taken from each machine and examined for Rockwell Hardness with the following results:

	Number in the sample	Sample mean	Sample standard deviation
Machine 1	16	41.6	1.6
Machine 2	9	40.8	2.0

Is there any significant difference between the hardness producing properties of the two machines?

We take the null and alternative hypotheses as:

$$H_0: \mu_1 = \mu_2$$

$$H_1: \mu_1 \neq \mu_2$$

We are given $\bar{x}_1 = 41.6$, $\bar{x}_2 = 40.8$, $s_1 = 1.6$, $s_2 = 2.0$, $n_1 = 16$ and $n_2 = 9$.

$$\sigma_d = \sqrt{\frac{16 \times 1.6^2 + 9 \times 2.0^2}{16 + 9 - 2}} = 1.83$$

Since the samples are small and the standard deviation of the population is not known, the t-distribution applies with:

$$t = \frac{|\bar{x}_1 - \bar{x}_2|}{\sigma_d \sqrt{\dfrac{1}{n_1} + \dfrac{1}{n_2}}} = \frac{|41.6 - 40.8|}{1.83 \sqrt{\dfrac{1}{16} + \dfrac{1}{9}}} = \frac{0.8}{0.76} = 1.05$$

The number of degrees of freedom is $n_1 + n_2 - 2 = 23$. From Table 6.1, at the 5% level of significance for a two-tailed test the critical value of t is 2.069. Hence we accept H_0 and conclude that the difference between the hardness producing properties of the two machines is not significant.

PAIRED VARIATES

In performing tests and experiments it is almost impossible to exclude undesirable variables. One way of overcoming this is to pair the test specimens. As an example consider a weather test on anti-corrosion coatings. The effect of sunlight, moisture, etc. will be minimised by placing the paired specimens in different atmospheres.

For paired observations we first find the difference, D, between each pair of values and then test the null hypothesis that the average difference is zero, i.e. $H_0: \bar{D} = 0$ and $H_1: \bar{D} \neq 0$. The mean and standard deviation are found from:

$$\bar{D} = \frac{\sum D}{n}$$

$$s = \sqrt{\frac{\sum D^2}{n} - \bar{D}^2}$$

where n = the number of paired specimens.

EXAMPLE 10

Paired corrosion resistance tests of anti-corrosion coatings Type 1 and Type 2 yielded the following data for the number of hours before the onset of corrosion. (The number of hours have been factored by a common amount.) On the basis of the test is the difference between the two coatings significant?

Paired specimen number	Type 1 coating	Type 2 coating
1	14	11
2	9	10
3	16	13
4	13	15
5	19	17

The first step is to find $\bar{D}$ and s.

Paired specimen number	x_1	x_2	$D = x_1 - x_2$	D^2
1	14	11	3	9
2	9	10	-1	1
3	16	13	3	9
4	13	15	-2	4
5	19	17	2	4
			$\Sigma\ D = 5$	$\Sigma\ D^2 = 27$

$$\bar{D} = \frac{\Sigma D}{n} = \frac{5}{5} = 1$$

$$s = \sqrt{\frac{\Sigma D^2}{n} - \bar{D}^2} = \sqrt{\frac{27}{5} - 1^2} = 2.10$$

Using the *t*-distribution,

$$t = \frac{\bar{D}\sqrt{n-1}}{s} = \frac{1 \times \sqrt{5-1}}{2.10} = \frac{2}{2.10} = 0.95$$

The number of degrees of freedom is $n - 1 = 4$. For a two-tailed test, the critical value of t at the 5% level of significance is 2.776. The result is not significant and hence we can say that there is no real difference between the two coatings from an anti-corrosion point of view.

EXERCISE 8

1) The mean lifetime of a sample of 60 T.V. tubes is found to be 8700 hours but the manufacturer states that the mean lifetime is 9000 hours. The manufacturers statement is to be rejected if the sample mean clearly contradicts it. Formulate null and alternative hypotheses.

2) In question 1 test the hypothesis $\mu = 9000$ hours against the alternative hypothesis $\mu < 9000$ hours if the standard deviation of the large batch of T.V. tubes, from which the sample was drawn is 1200 hours, using a level of significance of:
(a) 5%   (b) 1%

3) The breaking strengths of chains produced by a certain firm have a mean value of 1.8 kN with a standard deviation of 0.3 kN. By using a new technique in the manufacturing process it is thought that the strength can be increased. To test this a sample of 100 chains is taken and it is found that the mean of the sample is 1.90 kN. Using the 0.1% level of significance test if the new process has actually increased the strength of the chains.

4) A manufacturer states that his 5 mm rivets have a mean strength of 1800 N. A sample of 64 of these rivets is taken and their mean strength is found to be 1750 N with a standard deviation of 150 N. At the 1% significant level can the manufacturer's claim be accepted?

5) A sample of 64 castings was found to have a mean mass of 42.1 kg with a standard deviation of 4.8 kg. Could the batch from which they were drawn have had a mean mass of 44.0 kg. (Use the 1% level of significance.)

6) A supplier guarantees that each box of small electronic components will contain 250 components on the average. From a large consignment of such boxes a sample of 36 are checked and the average contents were found to be 248 with a standard deviation of 3 components. At the 0.1% significance level is there any reason to reject the supplier's guarantee?

7) An oil company will build a new petrol station if at least 200 cars pass per hour. For 20 randomly sampled hours the number of cars passing was counted. The mean number was found to be 208.5 with a standard deviation of 30. Assuming an approximately normal distribution can we reject the hypothesis $H_0: \mu \leqslant 200$ at the 5% level of significance?

8) The manufacturer of a new car claims that it will average at least 14 km per litre of petrol. For 15 test runs the car averaged 13.5 km per litre with a standard deviation of 2.7 km per litre. At the 1% level of significance can we reject the manufacturer's claim?

9) A manufacturer claims that the mean breaking strength of a particular type of cable is 8000 N. Strength tests were carried out on 10 such chains with the following results:

Cable number	1	2	3	4	5	6	7	8
Breaking strength (N)	7040	7600	8800	7400	8000	8400	7600	8000

Cable number	9	10
Breaking strength (N)	7920	8040

(a) Calculate the mean and standard deviation.
(b) Assess if the manufacturer's claim is substantiated.

10) Two machines are producing components to the same drawing. A sample of 36 items from machine A gave a mean length of 42.49 mm with a standard deviation of 0.025 mm. A sample of 64 items from machine B gave a mean length of 42.51 mm with a standard deviation of 0.020 mm. Is there any significant difference between the machines?

11) 15 electronic components made by manufacturer A gave a mean life of 1106 hours with a standard deviation of 75 hours. 12 similar components made by manufacturer B gave a mean life of 1180 hours with a standard deviation of 90 hours. Is there any significant difference between the two kinds of component?

12) Two different salt baths are used to harden a steel component. Samples are taken from each bath and tested on a hardness testing machine with the

following results:

	Number in the sample	Sample mean	Sample standard deviation
Bath A	12	40	2.1
Bath B	15	42	1.8

Is there any significant difference between the hardness inducing properties of the two baths?

13) Two laboratories X and Y analysed 8 samples of a chemical mixture. The following results were obtained for the percentage of a certain ingredient:

Sample number	1	2	3	4	5	6	7	8
Lab. X	8	10	9	11	10	9	10	9
Lab. Y	12	8	11	11	11	10	12	12

Are the differences between X and Y significant?

14) Paired wear tests of bearings Type A and Type B yielded the following data for the number of running hours before the onset of wear (the number of hours has been factored by a common amount).

Paired specimen number	1	2	3	4	5	6	7
Type A	12	9	10	11	12	8	10
Type B	10	11	10	8	10	9	10

On the basis of this test is there any significant difference between the two types of bearing?

15) A machine produces turned parts in large quantities. At the start of production a sample of 80 parts was checked and their mean diameter was found to be 11.63 mm. Some time later a second sample of 50 parts was checked and their mean diameter was found to be 11.67 mm. If the standard deviation remains unaltered at 0.08 mm, test if the mean diameter has remained the same.

16) A firm manufactures a certain type of thread. It finds that its mean breaking strength is 2.05 N with a standard deviation of 0.24 N. A new process is developed which, it is hoped, will significantly improve the breaking strength of the thread. To test if the new process is better a sample of 36 lengths of thread produced by the new process is tested.

(a) Find the critical value for the mean of the sample, at the 1% significance level, which will allow the null hypothesis, H_0: $\mu = 2.05$ N, to be rejected and the alternative hypothesis, H_1: $\mu > 2.05$ N, to be accepted.

(b) Calculate the probability of accepting H_0 when the mean breaking strength is actually 2.13 N, assuming that the standard deviation remains unaltered.

(c) By taking values of the population mean as 1.90 N, 1.95 N, 2.05 N, 2.10 N, 2.15 N and 2.20 N, draw an operating characteristic curve.

17) The mean size of the diameter of turned parts produced by a production process is 26.83 mm with a standard deviation of 0.3 mm. As production proceeds the mean diameter of the items increases due to tool wear. To test if the mean diameter has increased significantly, a sample consisting of 100 items is checked.

(a) Find the critical value for the mean of the sample, at the 0.1% significant level, which will allow the null hypothesis, $H_0: \mu = 26.83$ mm, to be accepted and the alternative hypothesis, $H_1: \mu > 26.83$ mm to be rejected.

(b) Calculate the probability of accepting H_0 when the mean diameter is actually 26.91 mm, assuming that the standard deviation does not alter.

(c) By taking values of the mean diameter as 26.70, 26.75, 26.80, 26.85, 26.90 and 26.95 mm draw an operating characteristic curve.

Chapter 8

Regression and Correlation

After reaching the end of this chapter you should be able to:

1) Plot scatter diagrams for bivariate data.

2) Describe the meaning of correlation as the degree of linear association between two variables.

3) Use the formula to calculate the product moment coefficient of correlation and test the hypothesis that the true value is zero using tables of correlation coefficients.

4) Recognise the difference between dependent and independent variables and choose the appropriate linear regression model.

5) Calculate the regression coefficients and use them to determine the appropriate regression equation and plot the regression line.

6) Use a regression equation to make predictions both by interpolation and extrapolation, if appropriate.

DEPENDENT AND INDEPENDENT VARIABLES

Consider the equation:

$$y = 3x + 2$$

We can give x any value we please and so calculate the corresponding value of y. Thus,

when
$$x = 0, \quad y = (3 \times 0) + 2 = 2$$
$$x = 1, \quad y = (3 \times 1) + 2 = 5$$
$$x = 2, \quad y = (3 \times 2) + 2 = 8 \quad \text{and so on}$$

The value of y therefore *depends* upon the value allocated to x. We therefore call y the *dependent variable*. Since we can give x any value we please x is called the *independent variable*. It is usual, when plotting a graph, to mark the values of the independent variable along the horizontal axis and this axis is frequently called the x-axis. Values of the dependent variable are then marked off along the vertical axis and this axis is often called the y-axis.

THE EQUATION OF A STRAIGHT LINE

The equation of a straight line is:

$$y = a + bx$$

where a is the intercept on the y-axis

and b is the gradient of the line (Fig. 8.1)

The method usually used to find the values of a and b is shown in Example 1.

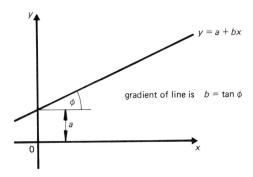

Fig. 8.1

When two variables are involved the given information is called *bivariate data*.

EXAMPLE 1

The bivariate data for two variables x and y are given in the table below.

x	2	5	7	10	14
y	8	17	23	32	44

Plot a graph and hence find values for a and b.

The graph is drawn in Fig. 8.2 and it is seen to be a straight line. Hence the equation connecting x and y is of the type $y = a + bx$.

To find the values of a and b, choose two points which lie on the line and find their coordinates. Thus in Fig. 8.2, point Q has the coordinates $x = 12$ and $y = 38$ whilst point P has the coordinates $x = 3$ and $y = 11$.

Substituting these values in the equation $y = a + bx$:

for point Q we have: $38 = a + 12b$ [1]

for point P we have: $11 = a + 3b$ [2]

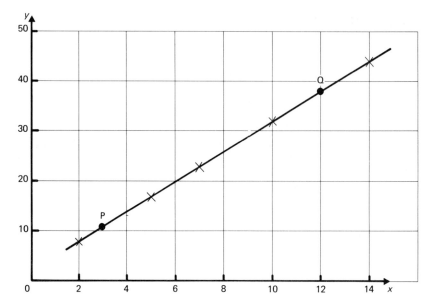

Fig. 8.2

Subtracting equation [2] from equation [1]:

$$27 = 9b$$

$\therefore$

$$b = 3$$

Substituting $b = 3$ in equation [2]:

$$11 = a + (3 \times 3)$$

$$a = 2$$

Hence the equation connecting x and y is:

$$y = 2 + 3x$$

We can now use the equation $y = 2 + 3x$ to find corresponding values of x and y not given in the original table. Thus,

when $x = 3.5$, $y = 2 + (3 \times 3.5) = 2 + 10.5 = 12.5$

Provided the value of x lies within the range of the original values (in this case, between 2 and 14) the process is called *interpolation*.

Suppose now we take $x = 20$. The corresponding value of y is $2 + (3 \times 20) = 62$. This value of x lies outside the range of the original values and the process is called *extrapolation*. An extrapolated value can usually be relied upon but in some cases it may contain a substantial amount of error.

As an example of this, consider the graph shown in Fig. 8.3 which gives corresponding values of e.m.f. and temperature for a certain type of thermocouple. Up to 700°C the graph is a straight line but after this

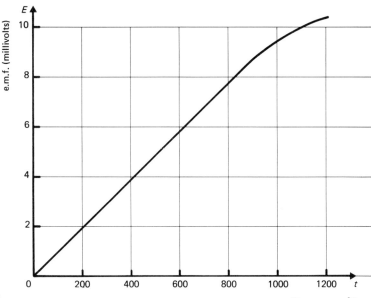

Fig. 8.3

temperature the graph is a curve. The equation of the straight line portion is:

$$E = 0.009\ 7t$$

If we use this equation to estimate the value of E when $t = 1000\,°C$ we obtain $E = 9.7$ millivolt. From the graph, however, the value of E is 9.4 millivolts when $t = 1000\,°C$. Thus, in this case, extrapolation has resulted in a substantial amount of error.

CURVE FITTING

Readings which are obtained as a result of an experiment usually contain errors in measurement and observation. When the points are plotted on a graph it is usually possible to visualise a straight line or a curve which approximates to the data. Thus in Fig. 8.4 the data appears to be approximated by a straight line whilst in Fig. 8.5 the data is approximated by a smooth curve.

Figs. 8.4 and 8.5 are called *scatter diagrams*. The problem is to find equations of curves or straight lines which approximately fit the plotted data. Finding equations for the approximating curves or straight lines is called *curve fitting*.

Individual judgement may be used to draw the approximating straight line or curve but this has the disadvantage that different individuals will obtain different straight lines or curves and hence different equations. To avoid this disadvantage the method of least squares is usually used to obtain the equation of the approximating curve or straight line.

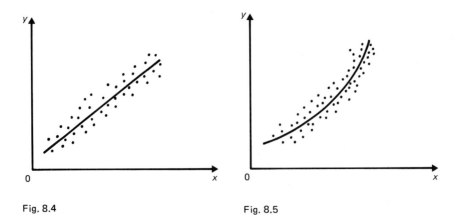

Fig. 8.4   Fig. 8.5

METHOD OF LEAST SQUARES

Consider Fig. 8.6 where an approximating straight line has been drawn to fit the given data. There is a deviation between the point (x_i, y_i) of the given data and the point (x_i, Y_i) which lies on the approximating straight line. This deviation is:

$$D_i = Y_i - y_i$$

The straight line having the property that:

$$\sum D_i^2 = D_1^2 + D_2^2 + D_3^2 + \ldots$$

is a minimum is called the best fitting straight line.

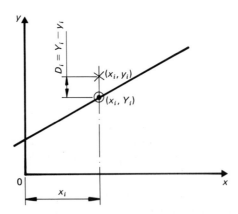

Fig. 8.6

THE LEAST SQUARE LINE

The best straight line approximating to a set of points $(x_1, y_1), (x_2, y_2) \ldots (x_n, y_n)$ has the equation

$$y = a + bx$$

It can be shown that

$$\sum y = an + b \sum x \qquad [1]$$

$$\sum xy = a \sum x + b \sum x^2 \qquad [2]$$

These are a pair of simultaneous equations from which the constants a and b may be found, n being the number of points. The equation obtained is called the *least square line*. Only the least square line will be considered in this book.

EXAMPLE 2

Corresponding values obtained experimentally for two quantities x and y are:

x	2.25	12.0	22.0	31.5
y	4.5	6.0	7.5	9.0

x and y are connected by an equation of the type $y = a + bx$. By finding the least square line determine suitable values for a and b.

x	y	xy	x^2
2.25	4.5	10.1	5.1
12.0	6.0	72.0	144.0
22.0	7.5	165.0	484.0
31.5	9.0	283.5	992.3
67.75	27.0	530.6	1625.4

$\sum y = 27.0$, $\sum x = 67.75$ and $n = 4$

$\therefore \qquad\qquad 27.0 = 4a + 67.75b \qquad [1]$

$\sum xy = 530.6$, $\sum x = 67.75$ and $\sum x^2 = 1625.4$

$\therefore \qquad\qquad 530.6 = 67.75a + 1625.4b \qquad [2]$

solving equations [1] and [2] gives:

$$a = 4.15 \quad \text{and} \quad b = 0.154$$

The least square line is:

$$y = 4.15 + 0.154x$$

EXAMPLE 3

The figures over show the results of an experiment to establish the relationship between the resistance of a conductor (R ohm) and its temperature ($t°C$).

t	25	50	75	100	125	150
R	20.7	21.6	22.2	23.0	23.9	24.6

(a) Find the equation connecting R and t if it is of the type $R = a + bt$.
(b) Estimate the value of R when $t = 121.1\,°C$.

(a) Here R is the dependent variable (corresponding to y) and t is the independent variable (corresponding to x).

t	R	tR	t^2
25	20.7	517.5	625
50	21.6	1080.0	2500
75	22.2	1665.0	5625
100	23.0	2300.0	10 000
125	23.9	2987.5	15 625
150	24.6	3690.0	22 500
525	136.0	12 240.0	56 875

$$\sum R = 136, \quad \sum t = 525 \quad \text{and} \quad n = 6$$

$$136 = 6a + 525b \tag{1}$$

$$\sum tR = 12\,240, \quad \sum t = 525 \quad \text{and} \quad \sum t^2 = 56\,875$$

$$12\,240 = 525a + 56\,875b \tag{2}$$

Solving these two equations gives:

$$a = 19.95 \quad \text{and} \quad b = 0.031$$

Hence $$R = 19.95 + 0.031t$$

(b) When $t = 121.1\,°C,$

$$R = 19.95 + (0.031 + 121.1) = 23.70\,\text{ohm}$$

REGRESSION

Suppose we are given several corresponding values of x and y which, when plotted, approximate to a straight line. To find a value for y corresponding to a stated value of x (which is not included in the given data) we first obtain the equation for the least square line which fits the given data. This line is called the *regression line of y on x* because y is estimated from x. (Note that the regression of y on x is determined by minimising sums of squares vertically.)

Sometimes we wish to estimate the value of x corresponding to a given value of y. In this case we use the regression line of x on y. This means interchanging the variables so that x is the dependent variable and y is the independent variable. (Note that the regression line of x on y is determined by minimising sums of squares horizontally.)

Generally the regression line of y on x is not the same as the regression line of x on y.

The regression line for y on x is:

$$y = a + bx$$

As shown on page 111 the constants a and b may be found by solving the following pair of simultaneous equations:

$$\sum y = an + b \sum x \qquad\qquad [1]$$

$$\sum xy = a \sum x + b \sum x^2 \qquad\qquad [2]$$

The regression line for x on y is:

$$x = a_1 + b_1 y$$

The constants a_1 and b_1 may be found by solving the following pair of simultaneous equations:

$$\sum x = a_1 n + b_1 \sum y \qquad\qquad [1]$$

$$\sum xy = a_1 \sum y + b_1 \sum y^2 \qquad\qquad [2]$$

EXAMPLE 4

The table below shows corresponding values of x and y obtained in an experiment:

x	20.7	21.0	21.3	21.7	22.0	22.3	22.7	23.0	23.3	23.7
y	22.0	22.1	21.7	22.7	21.7	22.7	23.0	22.7	22.8	23.7

(a) Find the regression line for y on x.
(b) Find the regression line for x on y.

x	y	xy	x^2	y^2
20.7	22.0	455.4	428.5	484.0
21.0	22.1	464.1	441.0	488.4
21.3	21.7	462.2	453.7	470.9
21.7	22.7	492.6	470.9	515.3
22.0	21.7	477.4	484.0	470.9
22.3	22.7	506.2	497.3	515.3
22.7	23.0	522.1	515.3	529.0
23.0	22.7	522.1	529.0	515.3
23.3	22.8	531.2	542.9	519.8
23.7	23.7	561.7	561.7	561.7
221.7	225.1	4 995.0	4 924.3	5 070.6

(a)
$$225.1 = 10a + 221.7b \qquad [1]$$
$$4995.0 = 221.7a + 4924.3b \qquad [2]$$

Solving these equations gives $a = 11.60$ and $b = 0.492$. Hence the regression line for y on x is:

$$y = 11.60 + 0.492x$$

(b)
$$221.7 = 10a_1 + 225.1b_1 \qquad [1]$$
$$4995.0 = 225.1a_1 + 5070.6b_1 \qquad [2]$$

Solving these equations gives $a_1 = -6.51$ and $b_1 = 1.274$. Hence the regression line for x on y is:

$$x = -6.51 + 1.274y$$

The two regression lines are drawn in Fig. 8.7 where it will be seen that there is an angle between them. Thus the regression line for y on x is not the same as the regression line for x on y.

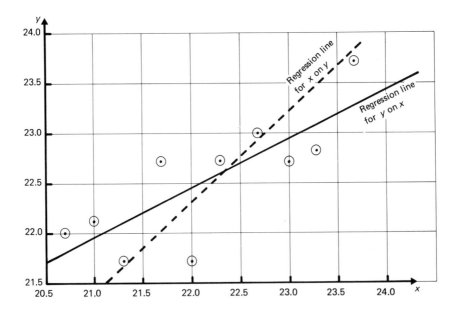

Fig. 8.7

CORRELATION

When corresponding values of two variables (x and y) obtained by experiment are plotted a scatter diagram like that shown in Fig. 8.4 is obtained. A rough relationship, or *correlation*, is seen to exist between x and y.

Correlation is closely associated with regression. We seek to determine how well a linear (or other) equation describes the relationship between the two variables. When the points on a scatter diagram are such that they approximate to a straight line, the correlation is said to be linear. Only linear correlation will be considered.

The correlation may be positive, precise or negative. For positive correlation (Fig. 8.8) large values of y accompany large values of x. For the correlation to be precise (Fig. 8.9) *all* the points on the scatter diagram must lie on a straight line. For negative correlation (Fig. 8.10), the values of y decrease as the values of x increase. If no relationship is indicated by the points on the scatter diagram we say that there is no correlation between x and y, i.e. x and y are uncorrelated (Fig. 8.11).

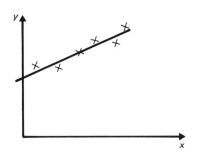

Fig. 8.8.   Positive correlation   Fig. 8.9.   Precise correlation

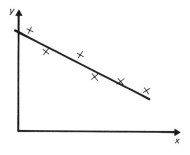 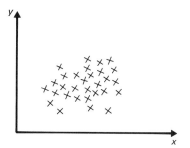

Fig. 8.10.   Negative correlation   Fig. 8.11.   *x* and *y* are uncorrelated

MEASURES OF CORRELATION

We have seen on page 113 that the least square regression line for y on x is given by the equation:

$$y = a + bx$$

The least square regression line for x on y is given by:

$$x = a_1 + b_1 y$$

These two equations are identical only if the correlation is precise, that is, only if all the points on the scatter diagram lie on a straight line.

We can often see, by direct observation of the scatter diagram, how well a straight line describes the relationship between two variables. In Fig. 8.8, for instance, we see that the straight line describes the relationship between x and y very well indeed. In Fig. 8.4, however, the relationship is not so well defined by the straight line.

Hence, in order to deal with the problem of scatter we had a measure of correlation.

THE COEFFICIENT OF CORRELATION

For perfect correlation the regression lines of y on x and x on y coincide. When the lines do not coincide we need some quantity which will measure the degree of correlation. The quantity used is called the *coefficient of correlation* and it is represented by the symbol r. The value of r may be calculated from the formula:

$$r = \frac{\sum xy - n\bar{x}\bar{y}}{n\sigma_x \sigma_y} \qquad [1]$$

This formula is known as the *product-moment formula for the linear correlation coefficient*.

EXAMPLE 5

For the data of Example 4, calculate the value of r.

Since $\quad \sum xy = 4995.0, \quad \sum x = 221.7, \quad \sum y = 225.1,$

$\qquad \sum x^2 = 4924.3, \quad \sum y^2 = 5070.6 \quad$ and $\quad n = 10$

$$\bar{x} = \frac{\sum x}{n} = \frac{221.7}{10} = 22.17$$

$$\bar{y} = \frac{\sum y}{n} = \frac{22.51}{10} = 22.51$$

$$\sigma_x = \sqrt{\frac{\sum x^2}{n} - \bar{x}^2} = \sqrt{\frac{4924.3}{10} - 22.17^2} = 0.960$$

$$\sigma_y = \sqrt{\frac{\sum y^2}{n} - \bar{y}^2} = \sqrt{\frac{5070.6}{10} - 22.51^2} = 0.600$$

$$r = \frac{4995.0 - 10 \times 22.17 \times 22.51}{10 \times 0.960 \times 0.600} = 0.787$$

The work in calculating the values of $\bar{x}, \bar{y}, \sigma_x$ and σ_y can be eliminated by substituting $\dfrac{\sum x}{n}$ for $\bar{x}$, $\dfrac{\sum y}{n}$ for $\bar{y}$, $\sqrt{\dfrac{\sum x^2}{n} - \bar{x}^2}$ for σ_x and $\sqrt{\dfrac{\sum y^2}{n} - \bar{y}^2}$ for σ_y in Equation [1]. After some rearrangement, etc. the equation becomes:

$$r = \frac{n \sum xy - (\sum x)(\sum y)}{\sqrt{[n \sum x^2 - (\sum x)^2][n \sum y^2 - (\sum y)^2]}}$$ [2]

using equation [2] the value of r for the data of Example 5 becomes:

$$r = \frac{10 \times 4995.0 - 221.7 \times 225.1}{\sqrt{[10 \times 4924.3 - 221.7^2][10 \times 5070.6 - 225.1^2]}}$$

$$= 0.787$$

Although there is a small difference in the value of r calculated by the two methods, this is due to rounding errors in the calculation of the various quantities used in the formulae. (The correct value of r is 0.798 4.)

If the equations for the regression lines of y on x and x on y are known then the following formula may be used:

$$r = \sqrt{bb_1}$$

Using the data of Example 5 we have (from page 116),

$$y = 11.60 + 0.492x$$

and $$x = -6.51 + 1.274y$$

∴ $$r = \sqrt{0.492 \times 1.274} = 0.792$$

For precise positive correlation, the value of r is $+1$. For precise negative correlation r equals -1. If the value of r is near to zero it means that there is practically no correlation between the variables.

THE SIGNIFICANCE OF THE CORRELATION COEFFICIENT

The corresponding pairs of values of the two variables x and y in Example 4 can be thought of as a sample from a population which contains all of the possible pairs of values. The correlation coefficient for the population is usually denoted by ρ (Greek letter rho) and its value is estimated by the value of r, the correlation coefficient for the sample.

To test the excellence, or otherwise, of the correlation between the two variables we test the hypothesis that $\rho = 0$ (i.e. that the true value of the correlation coefficient is zero.)

Table 8.1 gives critical values of the correlation coefficient for various levels of significance. The number of degrees of freedom is two less than the number of pairs of observations. That is:

$$\text{d.f.} = n - 2$$

EXAMPLE 6

At the 0.01 level of significance, test the significance of the correlation coefficient obtained in Example 5. Here $n = 10$ and therefore d.f. $= 10 - 2 = 8$. From Table 8.1, at the 0.01 level of significance, the critical value of r is

$$r_{CR} = 0.764\,6$$

The calculated value of r is 0.787 which is greater than r_{CR}. Hence we reject the hypothesis that $\rho = 0$ and conclude that linear correlation exists between the two variables. In fact, we are 99% certain that this is so.

Table 8.1.   Critical values of the correlation coefficient

Level of significance	0.05	0.01	0.001
Degree of freedom d.f.			
1	0.996 9	0.999 9	1.000 0
2	0.950 0	0.990 0	0.999 0
3	0.878 3	0.958 7	0.991 2
4	0.811 4	0.917 2	0.974 1
5	0.754 5	0.874 5	0.950 7
6	0.706 7	0.834 3	0.924 9
7	0.666 4	0.797 7	0.898 2
8	0.631 9	0.764 6	0.872 1
9	0.602 1	0.734 8	0.847 1
10	0.576 0	0.707 9	0.823 3
11	0.552 9	0.683 5	0.801 0
12	0.532 4	0.661 4	0.780 0
13	0.513 9	0.641 1	0.760 3
14	0.497 3	0.622 6	0.742 0
15	0.482 1	0.605 5	0.724 6
16	0.468 3	0.589 7	0.708 4
17	0.455 5	0.575 1	0.693 2
18	0.443 8	0.561 4	0.678 7
19	0.432 9	0.548 7	0.665 2
20	0.422 7	0.536 8	0.652 4

EXAMPLE 7

To see if there is linear correlation between two variables P and Q, the value of the coefficient of correlation is calculated and found to be $-0.920\,4$. 6 pairs of observations were taken. At the 0.01 level of significance is the value of r significant?

$$\text{d.f.} = 6 - 2 = 4$$

From Table 8.1, at the 0.01 level of significance,

$$r_{CR} = 0.917\,2$$

The calculated value of r is

$$r_{CALC} = 0.920\,4$$

Since r_{CALC} is greater than r_{CR} we reject the hypothesis $\rho = 0$. We are 99% certain that negative linear correlation exists between P and Q.

EXERCISE 9

1) The table below gives corresponding values of x and y.

x	1	2	3	4	5
y	8	11	14	17	20

Show that x and y are related by an equation of the type $y = a + bx$ and find values for a and b.

2) The following table gives values of x and y, which are connected by an equation of the type $y = a + bx$. Find suitable values for a and b.

x	2	4	6	8	10	12
y	10	16	22	28	34	40

3) A test on a metal-filament lamp gave the following values of resistance (R ohm) at various voltages (V volt).

V	62	75	89	100	120
R	100	118	136	149	176

R and V are connected by an equation of the type $R = a + bV$. Determine suitable values for a and b by finding the least square line.

4) During a test with a thermocouple pyrometer the e.m.f. (E millivolt) was measured against the temperature of the hot junction ($t\,^\circ$C) and the following results obtained:

t	200	300	400	500	600	700	800	900	1000
E	6	9.1	12.0	14.8	18.2	21.0	24.1	26.8	30.2

E and t are connected by an equation of the type $E = a + bt$. By finding the least square line find values for a and b. Hence find the value of E when $t = 840\,^\circ$C.

5) Find:
(a) the regression line for y on x,
(b) the regression line for x on y for the values given in the table below:

x	62	75	89	100
y	100	117	135	149

6) Find the regression lines for x on y and y on x for the values of x and y given below:

x	2.0	5.4	6.9	8.0	9.1
y	28	50	59	67	74

7) The regression line of y on x is $y = 24.0 + 1.2x$ and the regression line of x on y is $y = -12.0 + 0.7y$. Calculate the value of the linear

correlation coefficient and test its significance for 7 pairs of values at the 0.01 level.

8) Corresponding values of x and y are given in the following table:

x	20	40	60	80
y	101	108.1	115.1	122

(a) Calculate the product-moment coefficient of linear correlation.
(b) Test if the value of r is significant at the 0.001 level.

9) The following table gives the height (H cm) and mass (W kg) of 10 men:

H	160.0	180.3	182.9	172.7	190.5	167.6	172.7	193.0	180.3	177.8
W	65.8	71.7	70.8	67.2	74.0	70.4	69.5	71.7	68.1	69.9

(a) Calculate the value of the correlation coefficient.
(b) Test the significance of r at the 0.01 level.

10) The table below shows the distance travelled (D km) and the time taken (T days) by 8 lorries.

D	1320	344	1712	880	768	1472	2160	520
T	3.5	1.0	4.0	2.0	1.0	3.0	4.5	1.5

(a) Find the regression line for D on T.
(b) Find the regression line for T on D.
(c) What is the value of the correlation coefficient?
(d) Is the value of r significant at the 0.001 level?

Answers

ANSWERS TO CHAPTER 1

Exercise 1

1)

12.24–12.26	12.27–12.29
3	6

12.30–12.32	12.33–12.35
10	15

12.36–12.38	12.39–12.41
12	9

12.42–12.44	
5	0.03 kHz

2)

0–9	10–19	20–29	30–39
0	6	12	13

40–49	50–59	60–69
15	14	10

4) (a) 14.985 and 15.015 mm
   (b) 0.03 mm
5) 20.005 g
6) 176.7 cm
7) 199.95 mm
8) 162.25 Ω
9) 6.014 mm
10) 0.05 mm
11) 169 mm and 1 mm
12) 11.49 mm and 0.0145 mm
13) 168.19 cm and 6.19 cm
14) 641.5 hours and 95.58 hours
15) 101.92 kN and 7.33 kN

ANSWERS TO CHAPTER 2

Exercise 2

1) (a) $\dfrac{1}{6}$ (b) $\dfrac{1}{3}$ (c) $\dfrac{1}{2}$

2) (a) $\dfrac{1}{52}$ (b) $\dfrac{1}{13}$ (c) $\dfrac{4}{13}$
   (d) $\dfrac{1}{26}$

3) (a) $\dfrac{3}{7}$ (b) $\dfrac{3}{7}$

4) (a) $\dfrac{1}{5}$ (b) $\dfrac{1}{2}$ (c) $\dfrac{7}{10}$

5) (a) $\dfrac{1}{9}$ (b) $\dfrac{1}{6}$ (c) $\dfrac{13}{18}$

6) $\dfrac{1}{20}$ or 5%

7) $5\frac{1}{3}\%$

8) $\dfrac{4}{25}$

Exercise 3

1) $\dfrac{5}{52}$

2) (a) $\dfrac{1}{12}$ (b) $\dfrac{1}{4}$

3) (a) $\dfrac{4}{25}$ (b) $\dfrac{9}{25}$ (c) $\dfrac{6}{25}$

4) $\dfrac{9}{400}$

5) (a) $\dfrac{3}{10}$ (b) $\dfrac{1}{10}$ (c) $\dfrac{3}{10}$

6) $\dfrac{1}{15}$

7) $\dfrac{4}{9}$

8) (a) $\dfrac{4}{35}$ (b) $\dfrac{4}{35}$ (c) $\dfrac{6}{35}$
   (d) $\dfrac{4}{35}$

9) $\dfrac{1}{126}$

10) (a) $\dfrac{2}{5}$ (b) $\dfrac{13}{15}$

11) (a) 0.096   (b) 0.064
    (c) 0.24

12) (a) 0.46   (b) 0.88
    (c) 0.078 4   (d) 0.050 4
    (e) 0.12

13) (a) 0.02   (b) 0.98
    (c) 0.26

14) 0.99

15) 0.979

16) (a) 0.216   (b) 0.936
    (c) 0.385   (d) 0.593

17) 0.874

18) $\dfrac{19}{20}$

19) $\dfrac{59}{60}$

20) $\dfrac{95}{96}$

ANSWERS TO CHAPTER 3

Exercise 4

1) 0.814 5, 0.171 5, 0.013 5, 0.000 5,
    0.000 0

2) 0.596 7

3) (a) 4077   (b) 849   (c) 1000

4) 1181, 656, 146, 16

5) (a) 0.218 1   (b) 0.337 2
    (c) 0.555 3   (d) 0.444 7

6) 0.953 9

7) (a) 2%   (b) 1 and 0.99
    (c) 0.264 2

8) (a) 3   (b) 1.723
    (c) 0.225 2   (d) 0.577 9

ANSWERS TO CHAPTER 4

Exercise 5

1)

Number of defectives in the sample	Probabilities	
	Binomial	Poisson
0	0.590 5	0.606 5
1	0.328 1	0.303 3
2	0.072 9	0.075 8
3	0.008 1	0.012 6
4	0.000 4	0.001 6
5	0.000 0	0.000 2

2) (a) 0.367 9   (b) 0.367 9
    (c) 0.183 9   (d) 0.080 3

3) (a) 0.213 8   (b) 0.456 2

4)

Number of defects	0	1	2	3
Frequency	30	54	49	30

Number of defects	4	5
Frequency	14	5

$\sigma = 1.31$ $\sigma_{Poisson} = 1.35$

5) 0.195 4

6) 0.800 9

7) 0.442 2

8)

No. of defective items	0	1	2
Frequency	225	180	72

No. of defective items	3	4	5
Frequency	19	4	0

$\sigma = 0.844$ $\sigma_{Poisson} = 0.894$

9) 0.040 4

10) 0.264 2

ANSWERS TO CHAPTER 5

Exercise 6

1) (a) -1 (b) -0.5
    (c) 0.25   (d) 1.5

2) (a) 0.419 2   (b) 0.296 7
    (c) 0.569 4   (d) 0.944 3
    (e) 0.052 6

3) (a) 0.008 0   (b) 0.194 9
    (c) 0.082 3   (d) 0.015 0

4) (a) 0.022 8   (b) 0.006 2
    (c) 0.774 5

5) 1771

6) 115; 673

7) $\bar{x} = 20.00$; $\sigma = 0.013$

8) $\bar{x} = 170.03; \sigma = 0.76$
9) 0.192 2
10) 0.480 8
11) 4.75%
12) 2.74%

ANSWERS TO CHAPTER 6

Exercise 7

1) (a) 50.42 mm and 0.225 mm
   (b) 50.42 and 0.223   (c) 22
2) (a) 0.905 0   (b) 0.011 9
   (c) 0.003 3
3) (a) 8   (b) 4.472   (c) 8
   (d) 3.162   (e) $\mu = \bar{x} = 8$;

$$s = \frac{\sigma}{\sqrt{n}} = 3.162$$

4) (a) 635 g and 0.233 g   (b) 635 g
   and 0.232 g
5) (a) 19.048 mm   (b) 0.048 9 mm
6) (a) 172.7 cm   (b) 5.0 cm
7) (a) (i) $\frac{2}{3}$ (ii) $\frac{2}{5}$ (iii) $\frac{2}{10}$
   (b) (i) 25.3 ± 1.31 (ii) 25.3 ± 0.784
   (iii) 25.3 ± 0.392
8) (a) 14.1 ± 2.00%
   (b) 14.1 ± 2.87%
9) (a) 53.6 ± 0.60% mm
   (b) 53.6 ± 0.87% mm
10) (a) 53.6 ± 0.50 mm
    (b) 53.6 ± 0.65 mm

ANSWERS TO CHAPTER 7

Exercise 8

1) $H_0: \mu = 9000$ hours; $H_1: \mu < 9000$ hours.
2) (a) $u = -1.94$; $u_{CR} = -1.65$; reject $\mu = 9000$ and accept $\mu < 9000$ hours.
   (b) $u = -1.94$; $u_{CR} = -2.33$; accept $\mu = 9000$ and reject $\mu < 9000$ hours.
3) $H_0: \mu = 1.8$; $H_1: \mu > 1.8$; $u = 3.33$; $u_{CR} = 3.09$; accept H_1
4) $H_0: \mu = 1000$; $H_1: \mu < 1000$; $u = -2.67; u_{CR} = -2.33$; accept H_1
5) $H_0: \mu = 44.0$; $H_1: \mu \neq 44.0$; $u = 3.16$; $u_{CR} = \pm 2.58$; accept H_1
6) $H_0: \mu = 250$; $H_1: \mu < 250$;

$u = -4$; $u_{CR} = -3.09$;   accept H_1
7) $t = 1.24$; $t_{CR} = 1.729$;   accept H_0
8) $H_0: \mu = 14$; $H_1: \mu < 14$; $t = 0.69$; $t_{CR} = 2.624$;   accept H_0
9) (a) $\bar{x} = 7880$ N; $s = 476$ N
   (b) $H_0: \mu = 8000$; $H_1: \mu < 8000$; $t = 0.76$; t_{CR} at 5% level $= 1.833$;   accept H_0
10) $H_0: \mu_A = \mu_B$; $H_1: \mu_A \neq \mu_B$; $\sigma_d = 0.022$; $u = 4.36$; u_{CR} at 0.1% level $= 3.29$;   accept H_1
11) $H_0: \mu_A = \mu_B$; $H_1: \mu_A < \mu_B$; $\sigma_d = 85.2$; $t = 2.25$ t_{CR} at 5% level $= 1.708$;   accept H_1
12) $H_0: \mu_A = \mu_B$: $H_1: \mu_A < \mu_B$: $\sigma_d = 2.015$; $t = 2.56$; t_{CR} at 5% level $= 1.708$;   accept H_1
13) $\bar{D} = -1.375$; $s = 1.727$; $t = 2.11$; t_{CR} at 5% level $= 2.365$; $H_0: \bar{D} = 0$; $H_1: \bar{D} \neq 0$;   accept H_0
14) $\bar{D} = 0.667$; $s = 1.795$; $t = 0.91$; t_{CR} at 5% level $= 2.447$; $H_0: \bar{D} = 0$; $H_1: \bar{D} \neq 0$;   accept H_0
15) $H_0: \mu_1 = \mu_2$; $H_1: \mu_1 \neq \mu_2$; $u = 2.78$; u_{CR} at 1% level $= \pm 2.58$; accept H_1
16) (a) 2.14 N   (b) 0.022 8
17) (a) 26.92 mm   (b) 0.003 8

ANSWERS TO CHAPTER 8

Exercise 9

1) $y = 5 + 3x$
2) $y = 4 + 3x$
3) $R = 19.91 + 1.299 V$
4) $E = -0.008 + 0.030t$;   25.19 mV
5) (a) $y = 20.17 + 1.289x$;
   (b) $x = -15.64 + 0.776y$
6) $y = 14.96 + 6.472x$;
   $x = -2.31 + 0.154y$
7) $r_{CALC} = 0.9165$; $r_{CR} = 0.8745$; significant at the 0.01 level
8) (a) $r = 0.999\ 98$
   (b) $r_{CR} = 0.999$;   significant at the 0.001 level
9) (a) $r = 0.774\ 8$
   (b) $r_{CR} = 0.631\ 9$;   significant at the 0.01 level
10) (a) $D = 33.80 + 434.4T$
    (b) $T = 0.153 + 0.002\ 1D$
    (c) 0.955 3   (d) $r_{CR} = 0.924\ 9$; significant at the 0.001 level

Index